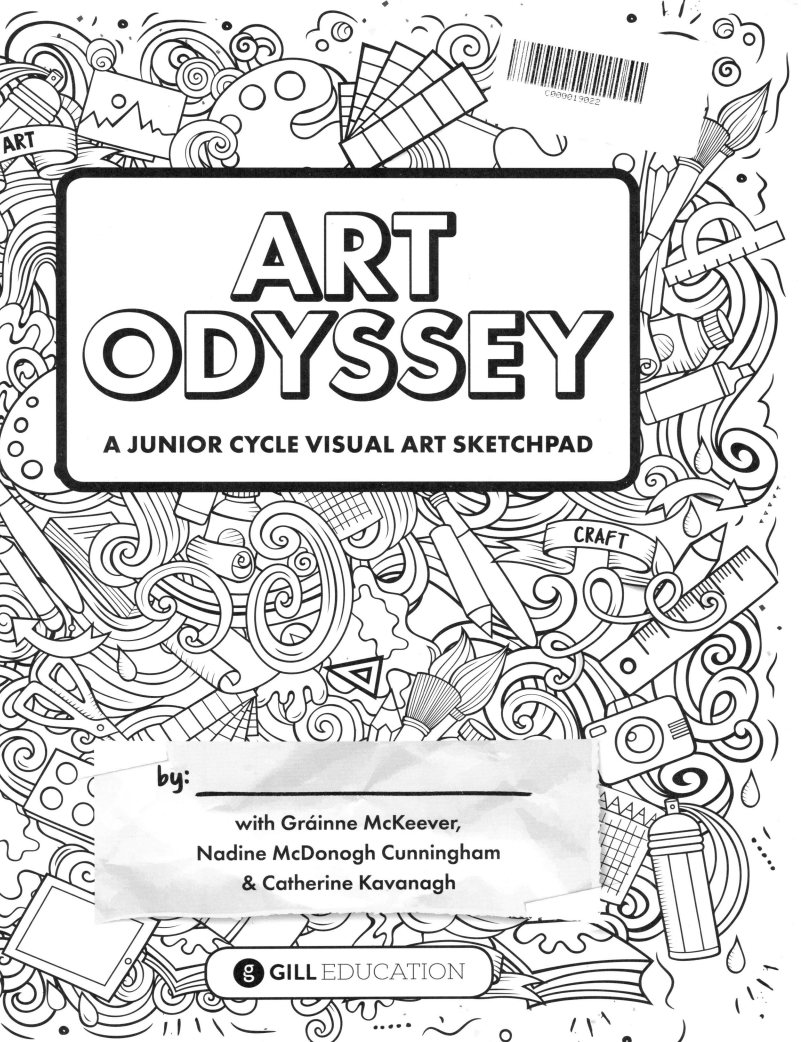

ART ODYSSEY

A JUNIOR CYCLE VISUAL ART SKETCHPAD

by: _____

with Gráinne McKeever,
Nadine McDonogh Cunningham
& Catherine Kavanagh

g GILL EDUCATION

Gill Education
Hume Avenue
Park West
Dublin 12
www.gilleducation.ie

Gill Education is an imprint of M.H. Gill & Co.

ISBN: 978-0-7171-83968

Design and layout: Sarah McCoy
Illustrations: Alan Batley/Graham-Cameron Illustration

At the time of going to press, all web addresses were active and contained information relevant to the topics in this book. Gill Education does not, however, accept responsibility for the content or views contained on these websites. Content, views and addresses may change beyond the publisher or author's control. Students should always be supervised when reviewing websites.

CONTENTS

JUNIOR CYCLE VISUAL ART

Welcome to Junior Cycle Visual Art! This sketchpad will guide you through your first year of this wonderful subject, giving you opportunities to develop your artistic skills, explore your imagination and consider visual art in the world around you.

The Junior Cycle Visual Art course is presented in three strands: **Art**, **Craft** and **Design**. Look around you and you will see that we live in a world where everything made by humans – from our homes, clothes and cars to our watches, desks and mobile phones – has been designed and created from someone's imagination. This sketchpad will help you to develop your art, craft and design skills so that you can create original works of your own and think about the process of how other artists, designers and craftspeople develop their ideas.

Alongside these three strands the Visual Art course looks at five important elements. These are shown in the diagram below.

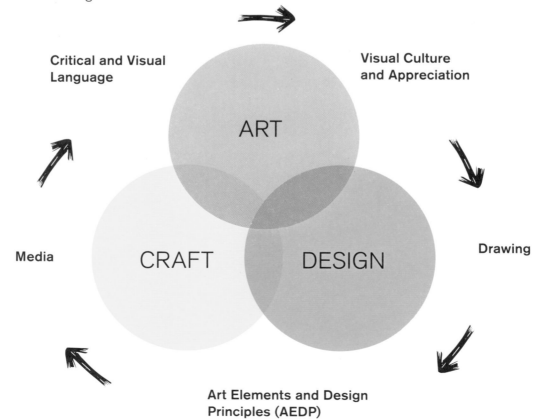

Critical and Visual Language

Visual Culture and Appreciation

ART

Media

CRAFT

DESIGN

Drawing

Art Elements and Design Principles (AEDP)

In First Year, through this sketchpad, you will begin to explore these strands and elements.

In Second and Third Year, you will complete Classroom-Based Assessments (CBAs) for Visual Art. This sketchpad gives you a place to practise and develop the skills and art processes that you will need for these Classroom-Based Assessments. You can find out more about the CBAs on page 135.

HOW TO USE YOUR VISUAL ART SKETCHPAD

When you study Visual Art, you use a Visual Art Sketchpad. It is your personal record of your creative journey and you should use it to document your work and to capture your ideas, investigations, explorations and even realised artwork. It will also hold any information you collect to help with your work, for example any research you do on artists, craftspeople and designers who interest or inspire you.

In First Year, you will use this book as your Visual Art Sketchpad. Sketch or jot down any thoughts and ideas you have as you work through it. Stick in pictures of artworks that influence your work, fabrics or materials that you like, or photographs of your own artworks that you create in class.

Your **Art Odyssey** **Sketchpad** will reflect who you are, your own interests, style and thoughts. Don't worry about making mistakes in here. If you are not happy with something or think you can improve it, make notes, alterations or develop your ideas further until you are satisfied.

Part A of this book focuses on **Practice** – here you will look at and engage with some examples of famous artworks; you will develop your drawing skills; you will explore different media and typography; and you will learn all about the art elements and design principles. **Part B** focuses on **Process** – here you will look at the Art, Craft and Design strands in more detail, and the process that a real artist, craftsperson or designer undergoes when they complete a piece of artwork. You will also complete three projects yourself – one for art, one for craft and one for design. You do not need to work through the book in any particular order. Your teacher will guide you on which pages to do and when!

As you use this sketchpad, you will come across this symbol. This symbol indicates that you are learning a key term to develop your Critical and Visual Language.

You will also come across the following icons, which represent the eight **Key Skills** of Junior Cycle. When you see each icon, there is an opportunity for you to develop these skills, which will help you in all your other Junior Cycle subjects.

 Managing Myself – This key skill will help you to set and achieve your goals, to make decisions and to understand how you work to the best of your ability.

 Staying Well – This key skill teaches us to be positive and healthy in our learning and our lives by considering our physical, mental and emotional wellbeing as we create.

 Communicating – This skill will help you to develop your art, craft and design vocabulary, giving you the language to present your ideas and to critique your work and that of others.

 Being Creative – When you see this link, there is a chance to use your imagination, to experiment and explore, and to try out your ideas.

 Working With Others – This link points out opportunities for you to engage with others. Whether it's through discussion or collaboration, you can learn with others.

 Managing Information & Thinking – This link encourages you to be curious, to gather, organise, record and evaluate information relating to your art, craft and design work, using a variety of media, including digital media, to share your creativity.

 Being Numerate – This skill is often used in art, craft and design. As we solve problems we encounter in our work, our mathematical reasoning helps us to move forward.

 Being Literate – The skill of literacy will benefit you in every aspect of your life, helping you to express your ideas clearly and develop your language.

Throughout the book you will also find hints, tips and reminders to help you on your creative journey.

Note to Teachers:
All of the artworks mentioned in this book are available as downloadable PowerPoints on GillExplore.

YOUR JUNIOR CYCLE ART ODYSSEY BEGINS HERE! 3 … 2 … 1 …

PART A: PRACTICE

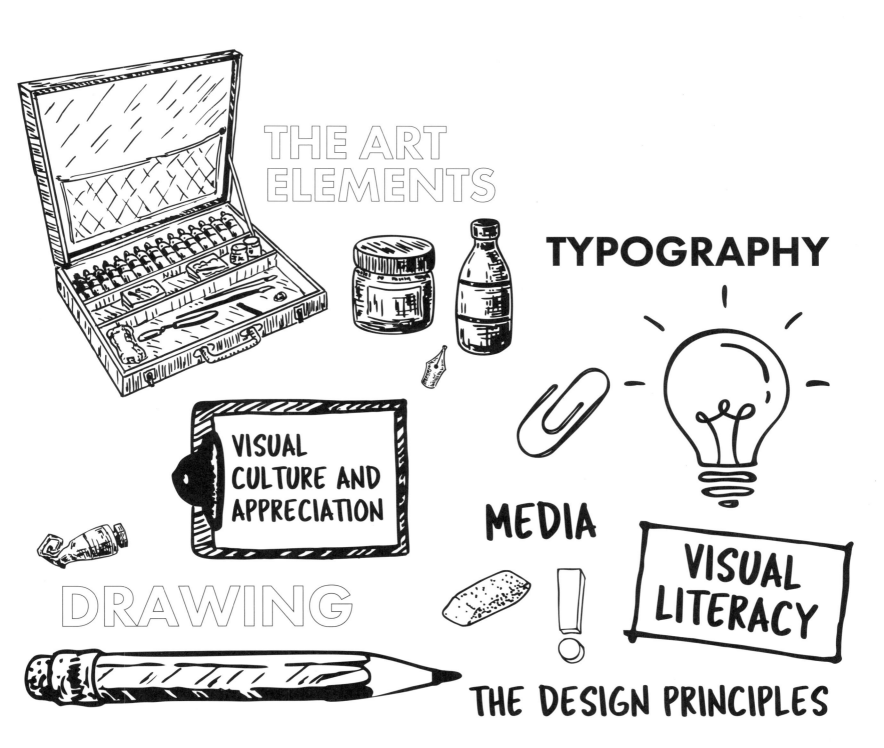

THE ART ELEMENTS

TYPOGRAPHY

VISUAL CULTURE AND APPRECIATION

MEDIA

VISUAL LITERACY

DRAWING

THE DESIGN PRINCIPLES

UNIT 1
VISUAL LITERACY

 Visual literacy is the ability to understand and make sense of non-verbal information that is presented to us as an image.

IN THIS UNIT I WILL:

❏ follow a design brief and show my understanding through drawing

❏ describe and discuss what I see in works of art

❏ discuss works of art and design from the past and present

❏ critique artworks using key language

LEARNING OUTCOMES:
1.2, 1.3, 1.8, 3.4, 3.7

ACTIVITY

Look closely at the following images and make notes of what you see. What do you think they mean?

_____

_____

_____

_____

_____

_____

_____

_____

ACTIVITY

Now create your own image or symbol, using colour, for a space centre or veterinary hospital.

VISUAL THINKING

Visual thinking is a term used in art when we try to make sense of a series of images. By making art and interpreting other people's art, we can learn to express ourselves and communicate the way we read these images.

Making a mind map helps us to explore our visual thinking. It helps us to successfully develop our ideas using a variety of art media.

Look carefully at the painting *Guernica* by the Spanish artist Pablo Picasso. He completed it in 1937.

Ask yourself: What can I see? What do I think is happening in this image?

ACTIVITY

Now create a mind map about *Guernica,* recording your **visual thinking** using words and images.

VISUAL REFLECTION

 Visual reflection is a term used in art when we look at our own work or the work of others, and we evaluate it and our response to it. It encourages us to make refinements and to consider alternative outcomes.

INVESTIGATION

Share your mind map from the previous page with your teacher and class group. Discuss your ideas.

ACTIVITY

Now use **visual reflection** to look back at your mind map and reconsider anything else you observe in *Guernica*.

Visual thinking and reflection can improve our critical and visual language.

INVESTIGATION

The Children of Lir by Oisín Kelly. Discuss how this public sculpture compares to Picasso's *Guernica*.

UNIT 2
DRAWING

Drawing is the process of recording your interpretation of the world around you. It is the foundation of art, craft and design production. Drawing is usually our first form of visual communication as children; we pick up crayons or pencils or anything we can find and we begin making marks.

IN THIS UNIT I WILL:
- ❏ use a variety of drawing techniques
- ❏ observe and record through drawing
- ❏ look at how artists work to understand their techniques
- ❏ make use of a variety of appropriate media

LEARNING OUTCOMES: 1.4, 1.5, 1.7, 1.14

ACTIVITY

Do you remember how difficult it was when you learned how to write? Using the hand that you don't usually write with, try to write your name here and keep within the lines.

ACTIVITY

Now you can write confidently, and your signature is uniquely your own style! Sign your name below.

Signature:

When we draw something for the first time, we don't always get it right. That is normal for all artists, craftspeople and designers. When we sketch, we experiment, and often those experiments do not work out. Those attempts are not mistakes; they are helpful ways of learning how we can best express our own unique view of the world.

Try not to erase anything until you have finished your drawing. You might be surprised at what you decide to keep.

ACTIVITY

Make a drawing of a pen from your pencil case.

ACTIVITY

Thumbnail sketches are a great way of figuring out your initial ideas without working on a large scale. Do three thumbnail sketches of an object. Sketch it from three different angles, experimenting with three different types of media.

There are three general types of drawing:

- ❏ **Sketches** help to quickly record an idea or information.
- ❏ **Development studies** are more detailed plans for a project. They help to refine the idea.
- ❏ **Realised works** are finished pieces of art, craft or design.

Develop two of your drawings using colour and your imagination.
How could your drawings be transformed?

ACTIVITY

Create a realised piece in the box below from your study of the object. It can be
realistic or abstract, a poster or mixed media – the options are endless.

PRIMARY SOURCE DRAWING

A **primary source** is something that we have seen for ourselves. A **primary source drawing** is made by drawing directly from something you have seen, so that your drawing is a first-hand account. This can include drawings you make from your memory or imagination.

Make a list below of any interesting primary sources you can find, and complete a drawing, using pencil, of your favourite primary source.

Exquisite corpse is a technique/game invented by the Surrealists. Artists such as Joan Miró and André Breton drew an image as part of a collaboration.

Working in small groups, you can play this game too. You will need paper and pencils. The aim is to compose a sequential drawing based on chance. The drawing is concealed and passed from person to person.

❏ Fold an A4 page horizontally into three equal parts.
❏ In groups of three, the first person will draw the head.
❏ Fold over the drawing and pass the sheet to the next person, who will draw the torso.
❏ Repeat this sequence until the page is full.
❏ Now open out the page and look at the drawing you have made together.

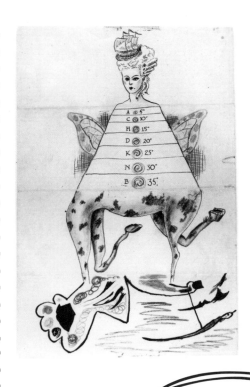

Remember – your imagination can also be an inspirational primary source.

Complete a primary source drawing from your imagination or memory of your favourite animal or bird.

Discuss how Surrealist artists Gertrude Abercrombie (1909–1977) and Salvador Dalí (1904–1989) used their imagination as an interesting primary source in their work.

BLIND DRAWING

Blind drawing is a form of observational drawing. You must focus on the object and not look at the page as you draw. It is a good way to practise hand–eye coordination, as your hand and eye must work together as you slowly record what you see. You can use a continuous line so that you do not lose your place.

ACTIVITY

Using a pen, draw your other hand using the technique of blind drawing. Do several drawings on the page using different coloured pens.

INVESTIGATION

Modigliani was an Italian artist who used continuous line drawing to plan his paintings and sculptures. Investigate his work.

Blind drawings are often very funny. Share yours with your class and have a good laugh!

GESTURAL DRAWING

Gestural drawing is a quick and simplistic style of drawing that tries to capture the essential parts of an object or figure. It includes only the essential lines that are necessary to capture the object or figure, for example the volume, the shape or the pose.

ACTIVITY

Find an object which you think is visually interesting. You will use this primary object as the focus of your work on this and the following page. Draw your primary source using gestural drawing. Perhaps you could use charcoal.

Jean-Michel Basquiat was an American of Haitian–Puerto Rican descent. He used gestural drawing in his work: above is an example.

INVESTIGATION

Explore some more of Basquiat's work. Describe and discuss his subjects and how you think he created his paintings. Also look at some works by Irish artist Francis Bacon and compare them to Basquiat's.

ANALYTICAL DRAWING

Analytical drawing involves closely examining an object and recording it in as much detail as possible.

ACTIVITY

Draw a realised piece from your primary source object below.

Realism is the practice of accurately representing a person or object.

Albrecht Dürer was a German artist born in 1471. His work is renowned for its fine detail.

INVESTIGATION

Look at Dürer's drawing of a hare. Describe and discuss the drawing techniques he used.

COMPOSITION

Composition is how we compose or arrange what is in a picture (our **subject matter**). It is important for artists, craftspeople and designers to consider where they place the various parts of their work, and to create areas of interest, or focal points, within their work.

An image can be broken down into foreground, middle ground and background.

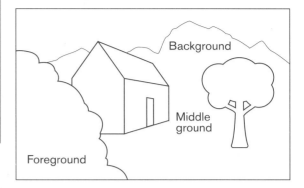

ACTIVITY

Have a go at creating a simple drawing of a streetscape with a clear foreground, middle ground and background.

The **rule of thirds** is a good way to lay out a balanced composition by placing points of visual interest on the intersecting lines (where the lines cross). Hokusai's *The Great Wave off Kanagawa* (1832) is a good example of the rule of thirds.

 Still life is a piece of art that represents inanimate objects.

Here are some examples of different composition shapes that help to frame an image.

Tondo (round)

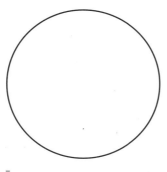

Portrait (vertical)

Landscape (horizontal)

ACTIVITY

Choose your favourite composition shape above and use your imagination to create a seascape in the media of your choice in the space provided. Make notes at the side to explain your composition choices.

PERSPECTIVE

 Perspective is used to create an illusion of depth or distance in a picture. It helps images to look more realistic. Before artists worked out how to use perspective in their work, paintings looked flat, and they didn't represent the three-dimensional world very well. The Renaissance was the period when artists developed this technique of perspective.

INVESTIGATION

Compare and discuss with your classmates the Egyptian painting from the tomb of King Tutankhamun from approximately 1350 BC with the Renaissance painting *The School of Athens* by Raphael (AD 1510). Examine the use of perspective in Raphael's painting and compare it to the Egyptian painting.

ACTIVITY

Draw an image of you and your friends dancing or playing sports in the style of ancient Egyptian art, without perspective, making the characters appear flat.

Compare the work *Las Meninas* by Spanish artist Diego Velázquez with *The Artist's Studio* by Irish artist Sir John Lavery. Research when they were painted. Do you think one artist was influenced by the other? How do these two painters use perspective in their work?

Velázquez: *Las Meninas*

Lavery: *The Artist's Studio*

 Overlapping perspective refers to objects appearing in front of each other. The further away the object is, the smaller it appears.

 ACTIVITY

Create a collage using overlapping perspective.

Linear perspective is dependent on a vanishing point; this is the place on the horizon where lines that are parallel in reality meet to create the illusion of distance, like train tracks. **One-point perspective** means that there is only one point on the horizon where objects become so small that they disappear. An artist might also use **two-point perspective**, where there are two vanishing points. This makes the work more complex.

INVESTIGATION

Wes Anderson is a film-maker who uses one-point perspective in much of his cinematography. Explore his work and find some stills from his films that show one-point perspective.

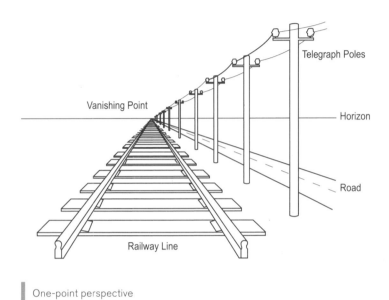

Telegraph Poles

Vanishing Point

Horizon

Road

Railway Line

One-point perspective

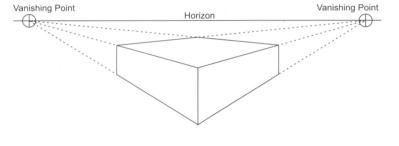

Vanishing Point

Horizon

Vanishing Point

Two-point perspective

ACTIVITY

Edward Hopper was an American artist. One of his most famous paintings is *Nighthawks*, which depicts a late-night diner in two-point perspective. See if you can complete the lines that lead to the vanishing point to the left of this work.

LIFE DRAWING

 Life drawing is a drawing we make of a live model. Artists use a variety of techniques to show realism in the human form.

During the Renaissance, artists created work that was inspired by the human form. *Vitruvian Man* by Leonardo da Vinci and *The Creation of Adam* by Michelangelo are examples of Renaissance art that explore the anatomy of the human form.

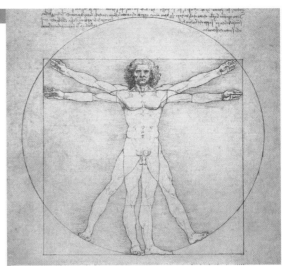

Da Vinci: *Vitruvian Man*

ACTIVITY

Analyse both artworks on the right and illustrate a detail from one of them in the space below.

Michelangelo: *The Creation of Adam*

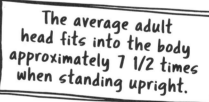

The average adult head fits into the body approximately 7 1/2 times when standing upright.

 Proportion in the human form is measured so that it can be drawn, painted or sculpted accurately. In art we use various guides to help us measure proportion.

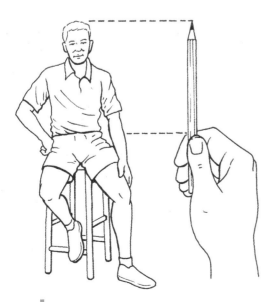

Use your pencil as a guide.

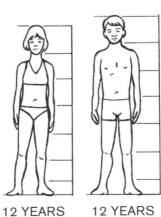

12 YEARS FEMALE	12 YEARS MALE
6 1/2 HEADS HIGH	

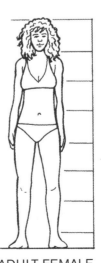

ADULT FEMALE — 7 1/2 HEADS HIGH

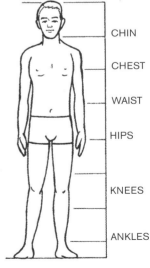

ADULT MALE — 7 1/2 HEADS HIGH

CHIN
CHEST
WAIST
HIPS
KNEES
ANKLES

These are very general average proportions. You can follow average proportions, but you must look carefully and draw what you see.

Sketch two life drawings focusing on the **proportion** of the model. Use a variety of gestural, analytical and continuous line drawings and explore different art media.

INVESTIGATION

The Knight and the Mermaid (1890) by English artist Isobel Gloag and *The Birth of Venus* (1485) by Renaissance painter Sandro Botticelli are interesting examples of proportion observed in the human form. Compare the two paintings and discuss your thoughts with your teacher and the class.

Botticelli: *The Birth of Venus*

Gloag: *The Knight and the Mermaid*

We use the word **volume** to describe a figure that looks solid and three-dimensional. To achieve volume, you first need to build a structure from the inside out, using lines and shading to indicate joints. **Structure** describes how an artist can build up volume and form when working directly from the human figure.

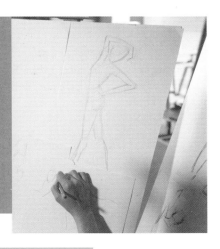

ACTIVITY

Using structure as a guide, complete a life drawing below and try to build up as much volume as possible in your work.

INVESTIGATION

Research the work of English artist Henry Moore (1898–1986). Now discuss with your teacher and the class how Moore used his life drawings to inform his bronze sculptures.

Gesture and **movement** are words we use in art to describe the human form when it is engaged in an activity.

French artist Auguste Rodin used a variety of continuous lines to describe the dancing movement of his models. Contemporary Irish artist Janet Mullarney also explores movement of the figure in her imaginative and surreal sculptures.

Rodin: *Cambodian Dancer*

Mullarney: *St Anthony's Tempter*

ACTIVITY

Be inspired by the work of these two artists! Choose some props from the art room. Create some interesting poses and make a series of two-minute continuous line drawings using a variety of media, **and/or** make some 3D maquettes in plasticine and record them in the space below.

Portraiture is the word we use to describe a work of art based on a person. A **self-portrait** is a study of ourselves.

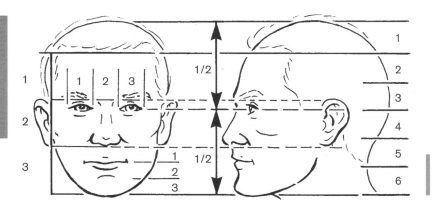

Front view and profile of the face

ACTIVITY

Work in pairs. Decide who will be the model and who will be the artist. Using the illustration above as a guide, complete a portrait in pencil of your model, concentrating on observing proportion. Now swap places.

Quentin Blake is an illustrator. Here is a picture he created of the Roald Dahl characters the BFG and Sophie. He has used artistic licence with the proportion of the BFG's features.

Facial expression in an artwork helps to describe feeling and mood. Photographers and painters interpret portraiture in different ways.

Kahlo: *The Wounded Deer*

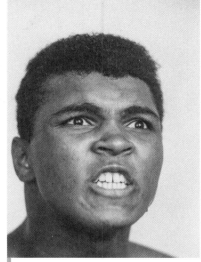

Weston: *Muhammad Ali*

What emotions do you think are expressed?

ACTIVITY

Take some photographs of your facial expressions. You can glue them in here or store them online for future Art classes.

How many facial expressions (happy, sad, angry, content, etc.) can you make?

Artist, songwriter and musician David Bowie experimented with his own face when he created his alter ego, Ziggy Stardust, in the early 1970s.

UNIT 3
MEDIA

 Media are the many different materials you can use to communicate your artistic ideas. For example, one medium is paint; another is pencil. You will learn how to use and experiment with many different varieties of media, some traditional and some more experimental.

IN THIS UNIT I WILL:

❏ communicate my ideas and understanding through drawing

❏ look at how artists work to understand their techniques

❏ discuss works of art from the past and the present

❏ examine artworks to learn what media have been used

❏ use appropriate media to create my own work

❏ look and record through drawing

LEARNING OUTCOMES:
1.4, 1.5, 1.7, 1.8, 1.13, 1.14

ACTIVITY

Shade in the boxes below with different drawing pencils to see what effects you get.

Can you think of all the different media you have used to create art?

Pencils are generally made of a thin piece of graphite encased in wood. They are graded on an HB scale. H is for hardness and B is for blackness, so a 2B pencil is lighter than a 6B.

You can also experiment with your pencils to create different effects.

ACTIVITY

Use your pencils to blend areas, smudge, cross-hatch and create planes using the flat side of the tip.

Paper is made by pressing together moist fibres, typically pulp derived from wood, rags or grasses. It is graded by weight. Cartridge paper is high-quality paper used for drawing. Standard photocopier paper is A4 size; A3 is twice the size of A4; A2 is twice the size of A3. Half of an A4 page is A5; half of that is A6, etc.

Other media you might use are: chalk or oil pastels, charcoal, markers, inks, and various types of paint such as poster paint, acrylic paint or watercolours.

Try experimenting with unconventional media, like drawing with a stick dipped in ink, or mixing sand into your paint, or painting with crushed-up berries or mud.

ACTIVITY

Fill in the grid below with various samples of media you can use, and annotate your samples.

INVESTIGATION

Ask your classmates what interesting experiments they have tried. Share your ideas.

Make a note of how you created your most interesting media. This will be very useful if you want to recreate it in the future.

Collage makes use of collected items to create a new image. You could use pieces of paper, photographs, fabric and other collected pieces to create an image by gluing them to a surface. **Montage** is a form of collage that uses cut-outs of whole images or parts of images to create a completely new one.

La Tristesse du roi, 1952, by Henri Matisse, Musée national d'art moderne, Paris.

Höch: *The Beautiful Girl* (montage)

The German artist Hannah Höch used montage in her work. She belonged to the Dada art movement, and she used montage to explore ideas about nonsense and free thought.

The French artist Henri Matisse used paper collage to create some of his work. He described his process of making artwork as both 'cutting directly into colour' and 'drawing with scissors'.

ACTIVITY

Experiment with collage, montage or paper cut-outs to create a portrait from your imagination. You could construct the face entirely from different colours, textures or shapes, or you could use cut-out parts of photographic images.

Mosaic is a picture or pattern produced by arranging small pieces of stone, tile, glass, etc., either randomly or in a particular order, to cover a surface. The pieces are held in place with a type of cement called mortar, and grout is used to fill in the spaces between the pieces to keep the water out.

Here are two examples of mosaic tiling. The first, from Pompeii, Italy, is from Roman times. The second is Islamic tiling from the Alhambra Palace in Granada in Spain. Analyse the two examples. What do you see in each that is the same or different?

ACTIVITY

Taking inspiration from what you have learned in this unit, use Henri Matisse's technique of paper cut-outs to create a design for mosaic in the line drawing below. Use colours and patterns of your choice. Leave space between each piece of paper to create a mosaic effect.

INVESTIGATION

Research the work of Antoni Gaudí, a Spanish architect who created amazing mosaic artworks and fantastical buildings. Find images of his work in Park Güell in Barcelona. Discuss this work as a class. Do you think Gaudí was inspired by the Islamic mosaics he saw in Spain?

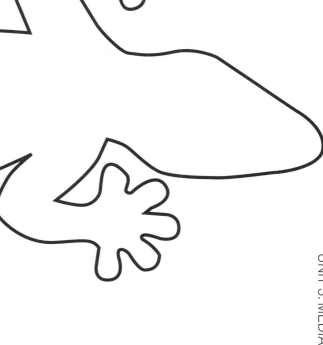

3D media are the materials we use to create three-dimensional art, craft and design.

ACTIVITY

Look at these examples of 3D work created using different media. What types of media can you identify? Discuss as a class and make notes about each work.

Cragg: *Elliptical Column*

_____

_____

_____

_____

_____

_____

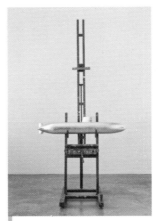

Cross: *Shark Heart Submarine*

_____

_____

_____

_____

_____

_____

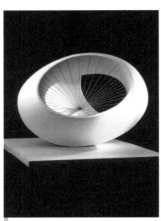

Hepworth: *Oval Form with Strings and Colour*

_____

_____

_____

_____

_____

_____

Degas: *The Little Fourteen-Year-Old Dancer*

_____

_____

_____

_____

_____

_____

Mosse: *Cookie Jar Old Rose*

_____

_____

_____

_____

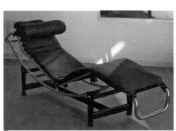

Le Corbusier: *LC4 Chaise Longue*

_____

_____

_____

_____

_____

ACTIVITY

Circle the 3D media below that you have used before. Highlight your favourite. Underline the media you would like to try.

Clay

Wire

Cardboard

Wax

Plasticine

Snow/ice

Wood

Stone

Papier-mâché

Plaster

Plastic

Recycled materials

Fabric

Paper

Digital media can be used as a way of not only documenting art, but also of making art. Photography, film and animation are the most common ways of creating art with digital media.

ACTIVITY

In groups of three, create individual 3D pieces of fruit using the **papier-mâché** construction technique. When they are complete, create an interesting still life of the pieces your group made. Consider where to put them, how to arrange them and the lighting. Photograph the arrangement, then print out your favourite photograph and stick it in the space below.

Can you think of any other ways of creating art with digital media?

UNIT 4
THE ART ELEMENTS

 The **art elements** are the building blocks of any work of art you create. The art elements are dot, line, shape, colour, tone, texture, form and pattern. Each element can be used in your 2D, 3D or digital work.

IN THIS UNIT I WILL:
- ❑ use art terms to analyse my work and others' work
- ❑ use a variety of drawing techniques
- ❑ communicate my ideas and understanding through drawing
- ❑ look at how artists work to understand their techniques
- ❑ look at how art elements are used by other artists
- ❑ make use of a variety of appropriate media

LEARNING OUTCOMES:
1.1, 1.4, 1.6, 1.7, 1.10, 1.14

ACTIVITY

What do you think each art element below means? Write and draw your response to each art element and include a primary source example for each.

Art Elements	Write	Draw	Primary Sources
Dot			
Line			
Shape			
Colour			
Tone			
Texture			
Form			
Pattern			

DOT

This is your starting point, the first mark on a page and the start of a line. A dot can be used in many ways. You can use a dot to add tone, to show shadow, or to create visual texture when you are doing observation drawing.

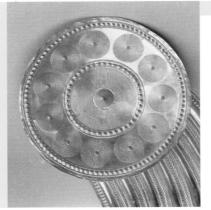

Repouseé is an ancient design technique that uses the art element dot to create patterns. You can see it here on the Irish Bronze Age gold artefact called the Glenisheen Gorget. It has been used to create circular and linear rows of beading.

ACTIVITY

Bring your pencil for a hop in the circle on the right. Create a pattern using dots and your imagination. Circle a selection of these dots in a different colour or use a variety of different colours and media.

One group of artists were very interested in what happens when dots of different colours are put side by side instead of the paint being mixed on a palette. Their technique was known as **pointillism**. The artist Georges Seurat developed this idea.

ACTIVITY

Below is Seurat's *A Sunday on La Grande Jatte*, painted in 1884. Add tiny dots of colour to the line drawing of a section of his painting on the right by using pure colour side by side and see how your eye mixes the colours when you stand back. This is called optical mixing.

Complete an analytical drawing of a real citrus fruit using dots to add detail, but make it by using mixed media of colouring pencils and markers that are the colours you see in the fruit, not the colour you think the fruit is!

Find out about other artists who use dots in their work, such as the Australian Aboriginal artist Emily Kame Kngwarreye, and the Japanese artist Yayoi Kusama. Discuss what you see in their works. Reflect on how their works make you feel.

Doodle with dots. Make as many dot marks and patterns as you can think of by using sequins, a hole puncher, printing with your finger, a cotton bud, a stick, bubble wrap and bottle tops. What else can you come up with to create dots?

LINE

A **line** is a point moving in or through space, like a pathway. It can move in any direction: vertically, horizontally or diagonally. It can be thick or thin, long or short, wavy, spiralling or broken up. A line can help mark the edge (perimeter) of an object or subject you are drawing.

Different types of line drawing include blind drawing, contour drawing, gestural drawing and analytical drawing (in line only). Line drawings can be really expressive and full of energy, or they can be very calm. They can also capture details and facts about an object or subject.

ACTIVITY

Bring your pencil for a walk below to create lots of different lines. Create a series of freehand **horizontal** lines across the page (don't use a ruler here).

INVESTIGATION

Use a pair of scissors to do a physical contour drawing of the perimeter of a primary source that interests you. Your result will describe the object's outline shape.

Start by holding your pencil at the base, then the middle, then at the very end. Consider how each line is different.

Under each word below, use one of your drawing pencils to make a variety of different **vertical** lines to express the words. Change the pressure of your pencil to vary the weight of your hard and soft lines.

Calm   Angry   Gentle   Sad   Energetic   Scared

Happy   Parallel   Hard   Slow   Soft   Long

Short   Thick   Thin   Broken-up

Now repeat the exercise, but make a **diagonal line** at the side of each set of lines in a different medium, such as pen, marker or ink and a stick!

The artist February James uses continuous line drawings. A continuous line drawing is when you don't lift your pen or pencil off the page.

ACTIVITY

Complete a continuous line drawing, in pen, of a face or another primary source object. Go slowly and try to capture all the details you see. Don't worry about crossing over lines – this exercise is all about really looking to see detail and keeping your concentration.

- ❏ **Directional line** can lead a viewer's eye through a composition or design.
- ❏ **Horizontal lines** indicate calm or rest.
- ❏ **Vertical lines** can show height, growth or strength.
- ❏ **Curved lines** give a feeling of smoothness.
- ❏ **Diagonals** show movement.
- ❏ **Zigzags** can show agitation or energy.

INVESTIGATION

Look at *Chalice* by Renaissance artist Paulo Uccello and Mary Swanzy's *Abstract Geometric Painting of Plants 2,* and examine the use of line in their work. Discuss as a class how they use line differently. Consider which work you prefer and why.

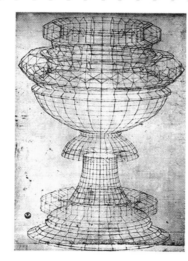

SHAPE

2D shape is a flat space that is enclosed by other elements such as line or tone.

Squares and rectangles can be associated with stability. Circles and curved shapes suggest movement and continuity. Triangles can lead the eye upwards. Inverted triangles tend to give a sensation of imbalance and tension. **Geometric shapes** are uniform, with straight edges and angles or precise curves.

ACTIVITY

How many geometric shapes can you find below? Use colour to help you identify them and write them underneath.

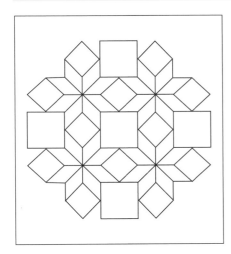 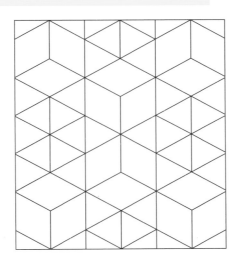 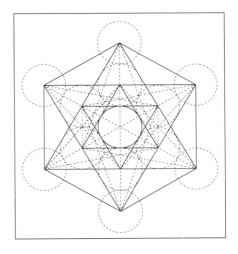

ACTIVITY

Use a ruler to help you create your own unique geometric pattern. Add colour.

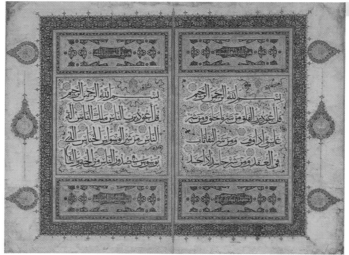

Ancient manuscripts such as the Book of Kells in Trinity College, Dublin, and the illuminated pages from a copy of the Qur'an held in the Chester Beatty Library display beautiful examples of geometric shapes.

ACTIVITY

Using colour, draw a detail from each example above.

Title of work:

Title of work:

INVESTIGATION

In groups, discuss what shapes you can see that are similar and different in both examples. Use your answers to annotate your drawings above.

3D shape is a solid shape that has three dimensions: height, width and depth. The 'D' in 3D stands for dimensional.

ACTIVITY

Below is a template that you can trace over or measure out to help you construct a 3D cube using paper. This will help you to understand how a 2D shape is used to create a 3D object.

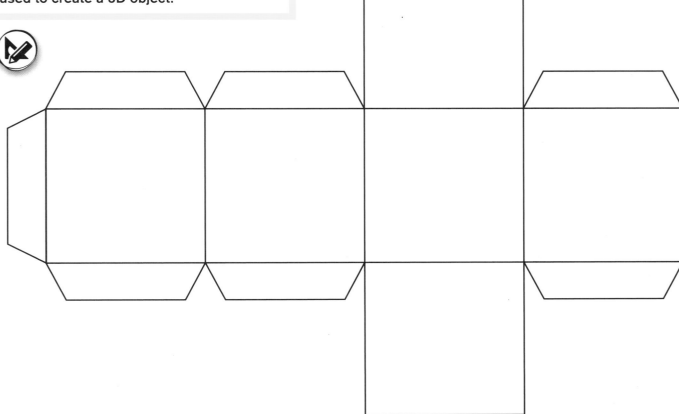

ACTIVITY

Now that you have made your 3D cube, complete a primary source drawing of your cube from observation. Remember – using **tone** will help the shape appear solid.

Organic shapes appear flowing and can be seen in every natural form.

INVESTIGATION

Look at the work of Georgia O'Keeffe, Joan Miró and Tony O'Malley, and compare how each artist used organic shapes in their paintings.

ACTIVITY

Complete a primary source drawing from observation of a natural object with an interesting shape.

COLOUR

Colour is the word we use to describe how our eyes see light. Dogs and cats, for example, see colour in a different way to us.

A **prism** is an object that can break up white light into its spectrum of colours. Raindrops act as prisms – that's how they create rainbows. In 1666, Sir Isaac Newton proved that white light is a spectrum of colours. He invented a disc of colours, which later became known as the Newton disc. When it is spun at high speed, the colours merge into white.

The **colour wheel** is a pie chart of the primary, secondary and tertiary colours. We cannot make primary colours, but using them we can create almost every other colour we need.

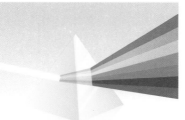
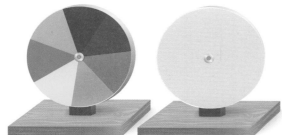

ACTIVITY

Apply the colours below.

RED	YELLOW	BLUE

Secondary colours are colours created when we mix two primary colours together.

GREEN	PURPLE	ORANGE

Tertiary colours are the colours we make when we mix a primary and a secondary colour together. For example, yellow mixed with green will create yellow/green. Blend yellow and green together in the middle. As the colour is mostly made of yellow, its local colour is yellow.

YELLOW	YELLOW/GREEN	GREEN

Colour in the colour wheel below and use it to find the complementary colours for the primary colours underneath.

Complementary colours are the colours opposite each other on the colour wheel. Because there is no component of one in the other, they make a well-matched pair and tend to stand out when placed next to each other.

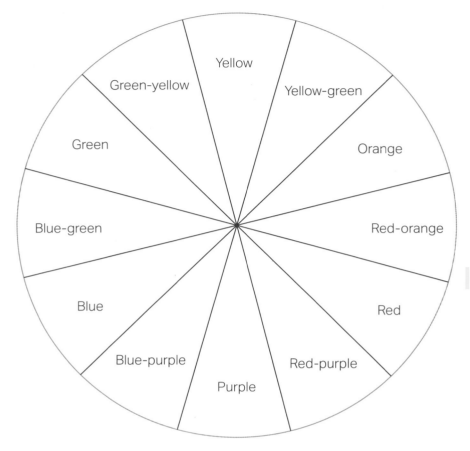

The colour wheel

Can you think of any examples of complementary colours that are used in packaging or advertisements?

Complementary colours

Red   = _____

Blue   = _____

Yellow = _____

INVESTIGATION

Examine the work of Henri Toulouse-Lautrec to see how he used colour.

C&UL A **palette** is the range of colours used in a piece of art, craft or design. **Saturation** refers to the intensity of colour. **Hue** is pure colour without any values. The **values** of a colour are its tint, shade and tone.
- ❏ A **tint** is when a hue is mixed with white.
- ❏ A **shade** is when a hue is mixed with black.
- ❏ A **tone** is when a hue is mixed with grey.

We describe colours as **warm**, **cool** or **neutral**. Red is a warm colour. Blue is a cool colour. Yellow is a neutral colour.

Warm colour

Cool colour

Neutral colour

Monochromatic means one colour and its values.

Analogous means 3–5 colours next to each other on the colour wheel.

ACTIVITY

Create three monochromatic colour palettes below: one using tint, one using shade and one using tone.

ACTIVITY

Create an analogous colour palette below.

Artists, craftspeople and designers often use colour to help them express their ideas. Colours can symbolise a variety of emotions; for example, blue can represent sadness.

Picasso: *The Old Guitarist*

Picasso had a 'Blue Period' when he painted human misery mostly in the colour blue. Edvard Munch was a Norwegian expressionist artist who painted *The Scream*, which symbolises his own anxiety with 'tongues of fire and blood stretched over the bluish black fjord.' It is a very evocative and expressive painting, using both colour and brush strokes to create the effect.

Munch: *The Scream*

ACTIVITY

What other emotions can you think of, and what colours might you use to express them? Fill in the chart below.

Emotion	Colour

Jack B. Yeats was an Irish expressionist painter. He was the brother of the famous Irish poet W.B. Yeats. His later work explored human emotion. One of his most celebrated paintings, *Grief*, uses colour to express the horror of war – its subject can be compared to Picasso's *Guernica*. The blue suggests sadness and his use of red and yellow symbolises rage and violence.

ACTIVITY

Wassily Kandinsky was a Russian artist and composer who often created artwork in response to music. Play or think of a piece of music that fills you with emotion and create an abstract response below.

TONE

Tone is the way that light falls on a 3D object. The parts of the object on which the light is strongest are **highlights**, and the darker areas are **shadows**.

Tonal scale in art helps you to achieve a range of different tones from the darkest shadows through various mid-tones right up to pure white for highlights.

Tone can be used to:

- ❏ create structure by balancing areas of light and dark
- ❏ convey a sense of harmony or tension
- ❏ indicate drama and atmosphere
- ❏ give the illusion of a solid three-dimensional object
- ❏ suggest qualities of light
- ❏ illustrate space and distance
- ❏ compose patterns across a picture or construction.

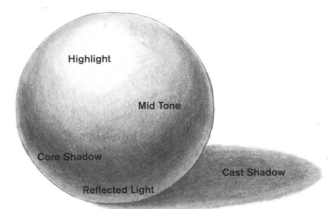

Light Source

Highlight

Mid Tone

Core Shadow

Reflected Light

Cast Shadow

ACTIVITY

Using your 2B pencil, draw as many tones as possible from dark to light.

Now repeat the exercise using different types of art media.

Shading is a drawing technique used to show tone in an artwork. There are many ways you can introduce shading into your drawing with your 2B, 4B and 6B pencils.

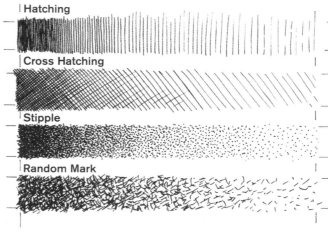

Hatching

Cross Hatching

Stipple

Random Mark

ACTIVITY

Use pencil to create your own examples of shading below.

ACTIVITY

In the space below, make a primary source tonal drawing from observation of a knotted tea towel. Observe closely the direction and source of light and consider how the light falls on the fabric.

Can you identify the source of light in this artwork?

Leonardo da Vinci's fabric study makes use of light.

TEXTURE

 Texture describes how the surface of something feels. It is used to add detail and interest. **Visual texture** is what we create in 2D art to describe the physical or tactile texture of our 3D world.

ACTIVITY

Take a coin and place it under the page to the right:

Now rub over it with the side of your pencil or a crayon to capture its texture. This is called a rubbing.

ACTIVITY

Find different natural and human-made primary source objects that have the following textures and write examples under each.

SHINY	FLUFFY	WOOLLY	ROUGH	GREASY	WET

DRY	SMOOTH	HARD	GRAINY	BUMPY	GLITTERY

INVESTIGATION

Review your mark-making exploration and drawing techniques so far to find ways of creating different textures. Make notes here.

Choose a selection from the previous page of the objects you listed with textures that interest you. Recreate samples of these textures in as many ways as possible using a variety of media and techniques.

Label your drawings to explain what you used and how. This will help you recreate these marks in later work.

Collect three different small examples of visual (e.g. pictures from magazines) or tactile/physical textures (e.g. wool, leaves, etc.) and stick them into the space here. Investigate each one carefully to recreate its texture using the most suitable media and technique beside it, giving reasons for your choice.

The artwork *Andromeda* (1999) by Irish artist Alice Maher and the work of Indian-born artist Anish Kapoor, *White Sand, Red Millet, Many Flowers* (1982) both make use of texture.

White Sand, Red Millet, Many Flowers, 1982 © Anish Kapoor, DACS London/IVARO Dublin, 2019

You could try sticking in a different ground here, such as sugar paper and use pastels.

ACTIVITY

Complete one very detailed analytical drawing below using suitable media and techniques based on your favourite primary source from your list of examples on the previous page.

FORM

Form is the art element that is concerned with dimension. When we draw on a page, it is a two-dimensional representation of an object that, in reality, has form, or three dimensions: length, width and depth. We can create form in our two-dimensional work by adding tone.

ACTIVITY

Look at the two drawings below and make a note of how you think they are different.

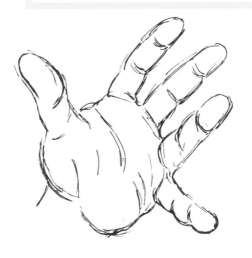

_____

_____

_____

_____

_____

_____

_____

ACTIVITY

Using tone, make a primary source pencil drawing of your own hand. Concentrate on achieving form.

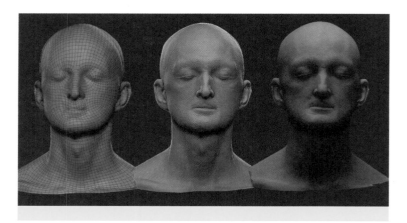

Contemporary artist Glen Southern uses a digital mesh to create form in his figurative work.

The early Renaissance artist Donatello sculpted Mary Magdalene using wood.

INVESTIGATION

In what way do you think Southern's modern digital techniques compare with the work of the early Renaissance artist Donatello? Discuss with your class.

Below are examples of still life compositions by Flemish painter Clara Peeters (1594–1657) and French painter Paul Cézanne (1839–1906). Both artists achieve form by observing light on various surfaces.

Peeters: *Still Life with Cat and Fish*

Cézanne: *Still Life with Apples*

Arrange a still life using your favourite colour media and an interesting light source. Complete a tonal study focusing on form.

The film director Tim Burton creates form in his characters using live-action and animation. Using your imagination as a primary source, create an alien life form. Experiment with your chosen art media.

PATTERN

 Pattern refers to the repetition of shape, line, colour, etc. If a certain item is repeated it can also be referred to as a motif in design terms. Pattern can also be described as the underlying structure of a composition. We shall discuss two types of pattern: organic pattern and human-made pattern.

Organic pattern has repetition but is generally not as precisely structured as human-made patterns!

ACTIVITY

Closely examine a leaf or another organic object. Observe the patterns in its structure and record them here.

Can you think of any other examples of organic pattern? Write your ideas alongside your drawing.

Human-made patterns are more geometric and tend to be quite linear and structured. Andy Warhol was an American pop artist who created patterns using print, often of images of celebrities or mundane objects like soup cans or boxes of Brillo soap pads.

Marilyn Monroe, 1967 © The Andy Warhol Foundation for the Visual Arts, Inc. /ARS New York / IVARO Dublin, 2019

Campbell's Soup Tins, 1962 © The Andy Warhol Foundation for the Visual Arts, Inc. /ARS New York / IVARO Dublin, 2019

ACTIVITY

Look around your environment for an example of human-made pattern – something that is an exact and geometric repetition. Now have a go at recreating the structure in a drawing on the right.

Robert Ballagh is an Irish artist and designer whose work is strongly influenced by pop art. He designed the last Irish punts before our currency changed to euros. Look at the patterns on the coins we use now.

Motifs are small symbols that represent something. For example, the harp is a motif that represents Ireland.

Can you think of any other motifs? Discuss with your class.

Research William Morris, a British designer who used pattern and motif in his work.

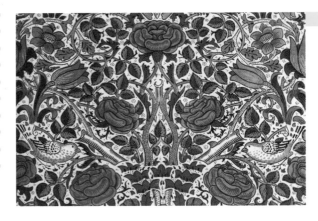

A **print** is an easy way to create a pattern because you only have to make one template.

ACTIVITY

You could make a print using a potato, lino or even your fingerprint to create a pattern here. Or you could simply draw a repeated design using one of the motifs you have already looked at.

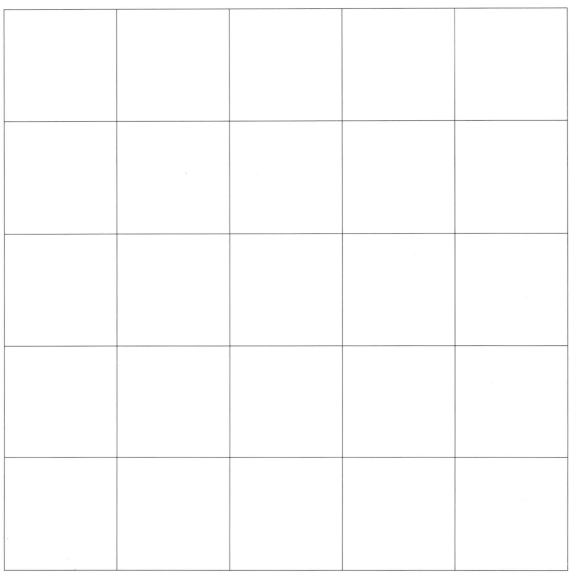

INVESTIGATION

Look at the work of Takashi Murakami, a Japanese artist and designer who uses colour and pattern in his work. What do you think has influenced his work?

UNIT 5
THE DESIGN PRINCIPLES

 The **design principles** are the building blocks of any work of art you create. The design principles are symmetry, tension, harmony, balance, light, space, scale and contrast. Each principle can be used in your 2D, 3D or digital work.

IN THIS UNIT I WILL:

❏ use art terms to analyse my work and others' work
❏ use a variety of drawing techniques
❏ look at how artists work to understand their techniques
❏ experiment with design ideas by researching and drawing
❏ use the art elements and design principles to help me examine designs by other people
❏ make use of a selection of suitable media in my designs

LEARNING OUTCOMES:
1.1, 1.4, 1.7, 3.5, 3.11, 3.14

ACTIVITY

What do you think each of the design principles below means? Write and draw your response to each design principle and include a primary source example for each.

Design Principle	Write	Draw	Primary Sources
Symmetry			
Tension			
Balance			
Harmony			
Light			
Space			
Scale			
Contrast			

SYMMETRY

Symmetry is the word we use to describe when something is the same on both sides of an axis – a mirror image. It is used to create order and balance in a design.

Asymmetry is when the two sides of an image are different and there is no central axis. This unbalances a work and draws attention to one side more than the other.

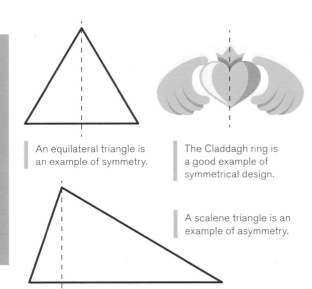

An equilateral triangle is an example of symmetry.

The Claddagh ring is a good example of symmetrical design.

A scalene triangle is an example of asymmetry.

ACTIVITY

Find and list six different symmetrical natural and human-made primary source objects.

Natural Objects

1. _____
2. _____
3. _____
4. _____
5. _____
6. _____

Human-made Objects

1. _____
2. _____
3. _____
4. _____
5. _____
6. _____

ACTIVITY

Using your line drawing techniques, create two analytical drawings exploring symmetry – one from your list of natural objects and one from your list of human-made objects.

Always label your drawings to explain what you used and how you used it.

ACTIVITY

Go through an old magazine and find examples of letters that show symmetry and asymmetry. Paste them in below.

Symmetrical Letter(s)	Asymmetrical Letter(s)

INVESTIGATION

Explore symmetry in architecture by looking at:

❑ the Custom House in Dublin – an example of Georgian architectural design
❑ the Heydar Aliyev Centre in Baku, Azerbaijan – an example of contemporary architectural design.

In pairs, describe and discuss what you can see in each of these architectural designs and then give your responses to the teacher to share with the class. Which design appeals to you most – order and balance or asymmetrical emphasis? Explain why.

ACTIVITY

Symmetry is used in art as well as design. Look at the piece *Sunrise* by Iranian artist Monir Shahroudy Farmanfarmaian. Consider how and why she uses symmetry in this piece. Make notes at the side of the image.

Look at the world around you and either draw or use a camera to document examples of symmetry and asymmetry in the design of everyday things, including local architecture. Print out your two best examples and stick them here.

BALANCE

Balance describes how we create visual weight in a composition. Artists and designers arrange art elements like line, shape and colour to balance their work to create feelings of stability or tension for the viewer.

The first example below is unbalanced, which is uncomfortable to look at. The second is symmetrically balanced – both sides are the same. The third is asymmetrical balance – there is an equal amount of visual weight on each side of the composition.

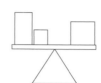

Here is an example of positive and negative shape creating **symmetrical balance**. Do you see a candle holder in the middle or two people facing each other?

ACTIVITY

Recreate this candlestick/faces image using the profile of your own face (if you can take a photograph) or a profile of the person who sits beside you. You can take turns.

The Samuel Beckett Bridge in Dublin was designed by Spanish designer, architect and engineer, Santiago Calatrava. It is a good example of asymmetrical balance.

ACTIVITY

Looking at the bridge on the left, does it look like it was inspired by any object in particular? Write down what balances both sides of this design, even though they are different.

_____

_____

_____

_____

_____

_____

_____

_____

ACTIVITY

Piet Mondrian was a Dutch painter who used colour to experiment with balance in his compositions. Look at this section of one of his works below. Do you think it is balanced or unbalanced? Discuss this with your class, and experiment with balance in a composition using primary colours.

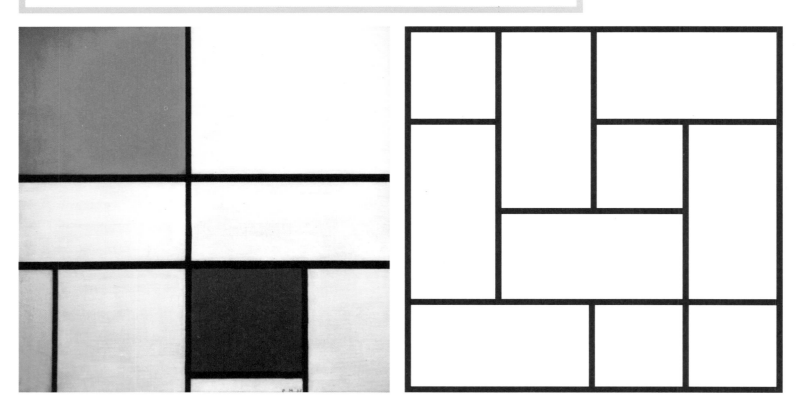

Radial balance is when the design emerges from the centre. Rays of sunlight are an example of radial balance. Maintaining a focal point is easy because it's always the centre.

Mandalas from Buddhist and Hindu traditions are good examples of radial balance. They are used to help people meditate and practise mindfulness.

ACTIVITY

Design your own mandala from the starting point in the centre of the circle.

**INVESTIGATION**

The rose windows at Chartres Cathedral in France are a great example of radial balance. Explore these stained glass windows and discuss them with the class.

Mosaic balance results from balanced chaos. The composition does not have distinct focal points, but it all works together. This technique creates a sense of rhythm.

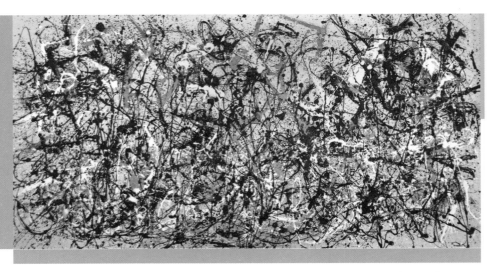

Autumn Rhythm, 1950 © The Pollock-Krasner Foundation / Artists Rights Society (ARS), New York / IVARO Dublin, 2019

Jackson Pollock was an American artist who used this technique often in his work. He used paint to create consistent splashes over large canvases.

ACTIVITY

Using any colour or tone you like, try to create balance in this honeycomb pattern. It is a good example of a pattern that occurs in nature – honeybees create a mass of wax cells in this shape.

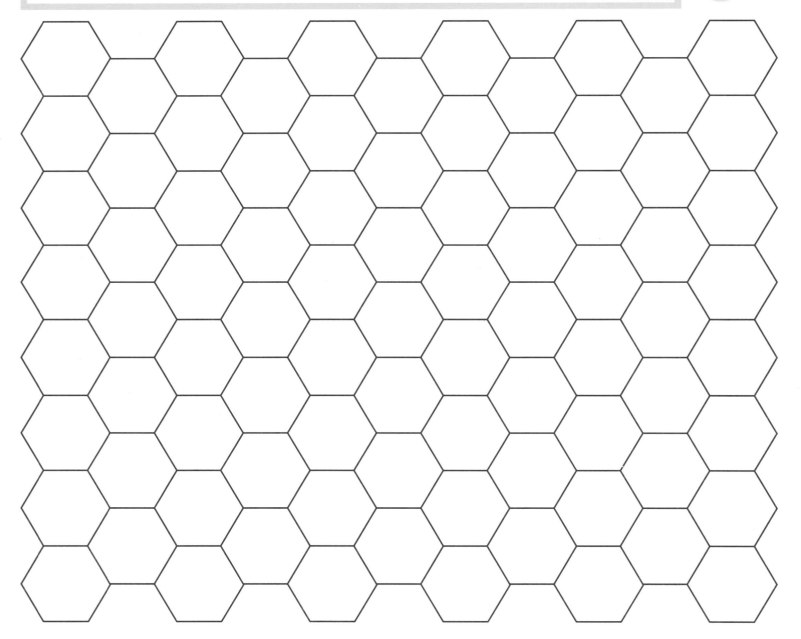

TENSION

 Tension is a word used to describe an imbalance in a work of art, craft or design. Tension is created by pushing elements together and/or by pulling them apart. This dynamic draws the viewer in and creates an interesting rhythm or flow.

American sculptor Alexander Calder (1898–1976) used line, shape, space, light and balance to show tension in his work.

In the examples below, the graphic designer has created tension using a flat square shape.

ACTIVITY

Use a ruler to measure and cut out five squares, each 3cm × 3cm, in black paper. Arrange them several times in the space on the right. Experiment with the layout of your squares until you are happy that you have created tension in your work. Now carefully glue the squares in place.

Did you successfully create tension in your work? Discuss your answer with your class.

Yvonne Farrell and Shelley McNamara of Grafton Architects designed the UTEC university campus in Lima, Peru in 2015.

ACTIVITY

Make a list of everything you see in the building on the left that you think illustrates tension.

_____

_____

_____

_____

_____

_____

_____

_____

Irish milliner Philip Treacy creates tension in his fabulous hat designs.

ACTIVITY

Be inspired by the examples of Philip Treacy's work. Design and make your original 'Thinking Hat'. *Experiment with a wide variety of art media.* Draw your realised work or take a photograph, then print it and glue it here.

HARMONY

Harmony is the word we use for a sameness or repetition in art, craft and design. The art elements and design principles appear to come together with ease and create a sense of order that we find aesthetically pleasing.

The Irish artist Roderic O'Conor (1860–1940) used textured strokes of contrasting colour to achieve harmony in his composition *Farm at Lezaven, Finistère*.

Can you find anything else in this painting that creates harmony?

Eileen Gray (1878–1976) was an inspiring Irish designer and architect who achieved harmony in her interiors and architectural designs. Look closely at her E-1027 house in France.

ACTIVITY

Using your ruler, make a harmonious line drawing of E-1027 in the space below.

Contemporary Irish artist Isobel Egan used porcelain to create harmony in her work *Circulus* (2016).

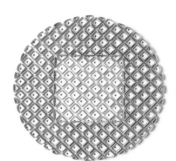

ACTIVITY

List and identify the art elements you think Egan used to achieve harmony in *Circulus*.

ACTIVITY

Using your imagination as a primary source, create harmony in a design for a sensory garden in the space below. *Remember to use the art elements and design principles you are familiar with.*

Diarmuid Gavin worked with nature to create harmony in his landscape design for the Westland Garden.

LIGHT

In art, craft and design, the word **light** describes areas of brightness as well as areas of light to dark tones. It can be used to show real light sources (where the light is coming from), to create areas of interest in playful shadows, or to bring the viewer's attention to something important – think of a spotlight on a stage. Light can be altered to affect our mood and response.

ACTIVITY

Natural or artificial lighting can be used to show shadows or highlights – do you remember this from when you studied tone? How would you turn the 2D circle into a 3D sphere by applying tone following the direction of the light source in the picture?

Label your photograph to explain what light conditions you used and why you selected it as your favourite example.

ACTIVITY

Find and group a selection of primary source objects of different shapes and textures. Observe and photograph them in different natural and artificial light conditions. Print out your favourite photograph and stick it here.

Stuccodores were master craftspeople working with fine decorative plaster during the 1700s in Ireland. They applied, by hand, decorative 3D forms – often of fruit, flowers, people and musical instruments – directly onto walls and ceilings. Light would play across these plaster works, creating dramatic impact and adding beauty to the room. These examples are in Castletown House, Co. Kildare and were created by stuccodores called the Lafranchini brothers.

ACTIVITY

Create a tile design in the space provided below. Take inspiration from a primary source that you find interesting. The tile should be in relief – that means not flat. It should have areas that are raised, as you will be exploring how light interacts with these raised areas.

INVESTIGATION

Look at the images of plasterwork above.

❑ What primary sources did the stuccodores work from?

❑ Discuss your observations in pairs and feed back to your teacher.

INVESTIGATION

Now make a 3D tile of your tile design. Model the form out of a modelling material such as clay or plasticine. Then paint it white or cover it with a layer of neutral papier-mâché. Observe how the light plays on your finished work. You could take photos of it with different light sources shining on it. Save your observations.

INVESTIGATION

Look up the meaning of the art terms chiaroscuro and tenebrism. Using these terms, describe how light is used in the following paintings: *The Taking of Christ* by Caravaggio (1602) and *Fishermen at Sea* by J. M. W. Turner (1796).

Light was also very important to the work of Irish stained-glass artist Harry Clarke (1889–1931). *The Eve of St Agnes* is an example of how he incorporated light in his work.

INVESTIGATION

As a class look at the full window of The Eve of St Agnes. Describe and discuss details from the window.

ACTIVITY

Create an illustrative design for a stained-glass window in the space below. Your design can be based on a poem that you like. Remember to explore areas of light in an interesting and expressive way.

INVESTIGATION

Realise your stained-glass window design by transferring your design onto card and cutting out the areas where you want light to shine through. Use a selection of different coloured translucent and transparent flat plastics and papers for the window panes. Stick these pieces to the card frame using glue or tape. When your window is complete, stick it up on a window pane or hold a torch behind it to see it shine.

SPACE

Space is the distance between people, places or objects in an artwork. Space can also be used in interesting ways to separate and connect images and typography.

Two-dimensional space is found on flat surfaces such as paper or canvas. Three-dimensional space can be achieved by introducing tone and perspective, overlapping objects, or changing the size and placement of objects.

Tone

Overlapping objects

Perspective

Changing size and placement

ACTIVITY

Using a **foreground**, **middle ground** and **background** can also help you to create space in your work. In each section below, draw exactly what you see from your own point of view.

Foreground Space directly in front of you	Middle ground Space behind foreground	Background Space furthest from you

Paul Henry was an Irish artist who created a wonderful sense of space in his landscape paintings of Achill Island, where he lived for a period of time. He also created space in his graphic design work using images and typography.

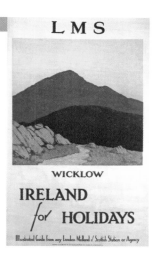

A viewfinder can help you to see space more clearly.

INVESTIGATION

Use a ruler, scissors and card to make your own viewfinder.

ACTIVITY

Look closely at the movie poster for *Ocean's Twelve* by the British designer Neville Brody. This poster is a good example of the use of space in graphic design. Using your viewfinder, choose a space that you find interesting in the poster and a complete a study of it below.

Positive space is the focus of an image. **Negative space** refers to the background. An equal amount of negative and positive space can bring balance to a composition.

Sky and Water I by M. C. Escher is an example of a balanced composition using positive and negative space.

ACTIVITY

Complete a study of Escher's woodcut using two complementary colours.

Have you successfully achieved balance in your work?

SCALE

Scale is used to express size relationships in an artwork. Scale is also used in maps: they are tiny scale drawings of locations in an exact ratio or proportion, so 1cm on the map might be equal to 100km in reality. Scale can be very useful!

Chuck Close is an artist who makes very large-scale portraits using this technique. He takes photographs first and then draws a grid over them and enlarges them into huge paintings like the one shown here, which in real life measures 9 feet by 7 feet!

Close: *Mark*

ACTIVITY

Recreate the portrait by Chuck Close in the grid below. First draw a grid over the image above, by measuring three equal spaces across the top and the same along the side. Then copy the portrait, box by box, into the larger grid. The ratio of the drawing is 1:2 – that's twice the size. You could label the boxes 1–3 across the top and A–C down the side to help you keep track of the boxes.

Claes Oldenburg is an artist who creates large-scale artworks based on items that are usually quite small, such as clothes pegs, food and matchsticks.

On a separate piece of paper, design a sculpture of a an object you could enlarge to a much bigger scale and place in the Burren landscape of County Clare. Cut out the picture of your sculpture and stick it into the landscape photo below.

INVESTIGATION

Have a look at the work of Christo and Jeanne-Claude, two artists who collaborate on large-scale works. Compare it to the work of Russian sculptor Salavat Fidai, who carves tiny pieces on pencil tips. Discuss with your classmates.

CONTRAST

Contrast happens when we arrange objects/subjects together that are opposites to each other, such as light and dark, rough and smooth, big and small. We might decide we want something to stand out because it is important in our design, and using contrast can be a good way of doing this and creating visual interest.

ACTIVITY

Consider these two pieces of design on the right, using your knowledge of the art elements and design principles. How have the designers Saul Bass and Lauren Child used contrast in their works? Make notes in the spaces provided.

Saul Bass

Lauren Child

INVESTIGATION

As a class, discuss your findings in pairs, then feed back to your teacher. Add to your list, using a different colour, any other observations made by your class that interest you.

Sketch the design from the previous page that you feel has the most interesting contrast. This will help you analyse the designer's techniques.

ACTIVITY

Write down two contrasting items under each of the following art elements.

Texture	Tone	Shape

Choose the pair of objects from the previous page that appeal to you most. Using primary source objects, complete a detailed observational drawing of the contrasting pair.

UNIT 6
TYPOGRAPHY

Typography is the art and design of lettering. **Typeface** is the word we use for a specific design of an alphabet – you might know it as a font. You may have heard the names of some typefaces, such as **Comic Sans**, Times New Roman or **Arial**. When you use Word on a computer you can click on the font function on the toolbar to see a selection of typefaces. These have all been created by designers called **typographers**.

IN THIS UNIT I WILL:

❏ use key design language to help me discuss design work
❏ experiment with design ideas by researching and drawing
❏ create my own piece of original design
❏ use the art elements and design principles to help me examine designs by other people

LEARNING OUTCOMES: 3.1, 3.5, 3.6, 3.11

ACTIVITY

Have you ever noticed how many different ways a word can be written? Look at the examples below. Then create your own version of 'Word' in the box.

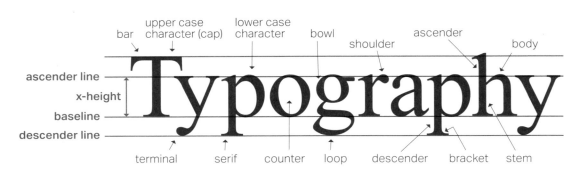

Below is a breakdown of each part of the letters in a piece of typography.

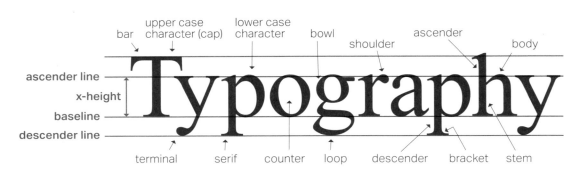

INVESTIGATION

Write your name. Which of these parts of the letters are there in your name? Discuss what you find with your classmate.

Select a few different typefaces that you find interesting from newspapers, magazines or flyers and stick them here.

Review and make quick notes beside each typeface to describe the art elements or design principles that have been used to create them.

ACTIVITY

Below are some **typography key words** you should consider when creating or discussing typography. Use your favourite colour pen or pencil to investigate each.

Key Words	Exercise
Upper case – the words are written all in CAPITAL LETTERS. **Lower case** – the words are written all in lower case letters.	Write 'word' all in upper case and then all in lower case: WORD word
Serif/sans serif – serif has details on the ends of the letter stroke (hats and tails). **Sans Serif** is plain, without tails and hats, like this!	Which do you prefer? Write 'word' in serif or sans serif: word
Weight – the thickness of the typeface. It can be light, regular, **bold**. You can create emphasis on a **word** by changing its weight, or using *italics*, <u>underlining</u> or playing with **scale**.	Write 'word' in a way that makes it bold: Word
Expressive typography – this when you use typography to capture the meaning or mood of what you are writing. The typeface, your choice of colour, and your use of emphasis can all contribute to this.	Use the space to write 'word' in a typeface that you think looks happy or sad: word
Kerning – the **s p a c e s** between characters (characters are letters, numbers, commas, exclamation marks, etc.) AV Wa AV Wa No kerning No kerning Kerning applied Kerning applied	Use a red pencil and colour between the letters here to show the kerning: Word

Using the key words on the previous page to help inspire you, create a piece of original typography.

❏ First make a mind map of your favourite things (colours, hobbies, animals, etc.).

❏ Then choose a typeface from the selection you stuck in or a named one that you know.

❏ Now change/adapt this typeface to write your name in a personal and expressive way.

❏ Use a ruler to help you measure your spacing carefully.

Always label your drawings to explain how and why you used them.

Mind map

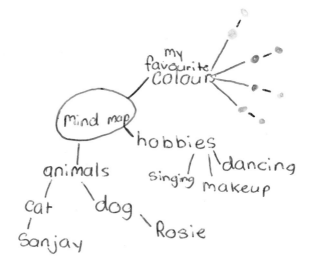

Design your font

font

word

UNIT 7
VISUAL CULTURE AND APPRECIATION

ART ENGAGEMENT

Art engagement happens when you experience real works of art, craft and design by looking closely, asking yourself questions about what you are seeing and getting really curious about how and why something was created.

IN THIS UNIT I WILL:

❏ use key language to help me discuss art, craft and design work

❏ critique art, craft and design works using art language

❏ make use of drawing to communicate my understanding of the world

❏ look at how a selection of artworks were created

❏ discuss works of art from the past and the present

❏ debate the value of artworks

LEARNING OUTCOMES:
1.1, 1.3, 1.6, 1.7, 1.8, 1.9, 3.1, 3.3

We have already looked at many famous artworks in this book, but the best way to engage with art is in person, by visiting galleries, exhibitions and museums. However, if you can't visit in person, you can go online. This gives you the chance to virtually travel to see famous artworks in spaces like the Louvre in Paris, the Prado in Madrid, the Uffizi in Florence and MoMA in New York. Perhaps an artist or other professional practitioner or maker could visit your school, or you could go to their studio to see them working. Don't forget, not all art is in galleries! You can find it in the world around you too.

ACTIVITY

Record the places near you where you can view art, craft and design. Also make a note of any other places where you see art, craft and design.

Your local places	Any other places

PUBLIC ART

Public art is the term we use to describe artworks in our local environment. They are often located in towns and cities, along motorways and in front of large buildings.

The Irish sculptor Rowan Gillespie's *Famine Memorial* is an example of public sculpture. It is located beside the River Liffey in Dublin, on Custom House Quay.

INVESTIGATION

As a class, discuss the piece *Famine Memorial*.
- ❑ What do you see?
- ❑ What do you think it is made of?
- ❑ Why do you think it was created?
- ❑ Why do you think it was located on the quayside of the River Liffey in Dublin?
- ❑ Did you know that there is a corresponding piece in Toronto, Canada called *The Arrival*? What can you find out about that public sculpture?

Why do you think public art is needed? Think of all of the possibilities.

ACTIVITY

Think about a piece of public art you have seen that you really like.
Use any media or technique of your choice to draw it here. Label your drawing with as much information as you can about this work. There are some questions below to get you started. You could use the internet to help you with your research.

Where is it located?
What is the title of the work, or what is it known as?
What is the artist's name?
What is it made of?
How do you think it was made?

ART FOR CHANGE

Art is often used to express the artist's response to their environment. If the artist lives in a place where there is social, economic or political unrest, that might impact their work. They might use their art to express their feelings about what is happening to them or their world, and in this way educate others or create empathy or outrage, which can lead to change.

Can you think of any political changes or social issues in the news at the moment? Have you noticed any artistic response to this?

ACTIVITY

Joe Caslin is an Irish artist and Art teacher who has created many pieces of artwork in response to social and political issues. Annotate this piece of his work below with your thoughts on what it is about, where and when it was produced and its significance in terms of activism.

Artists often use the environment they are in as the canvas for their work, by painting on walls or hoardings to convey their message. In Northern Ireland, political artists often painted murals on the gable ends of houses displaying images of British and Irish symbols.

Diego Rivera was a Mexican artist who helped to establish the Mexican mural movement. Many of his frescos and murals were about the history and politics of Mexico.

Rivera: *Glorious Victory*

INVESTIGATION

As a class, discuss what Diego Rivera's mural *Glorious Victory* (1954) could be about. Try to find out the real story behind this work.

ACTIVITY

If you had to create a mural on the end of your street, what would you draw to represent your area? Are there things you are proud of? Are there things you feel strongly should be changed? Would you feel confident about presenting that idea in such a public way? Create a mural on the gable below with pictures or writing or both.

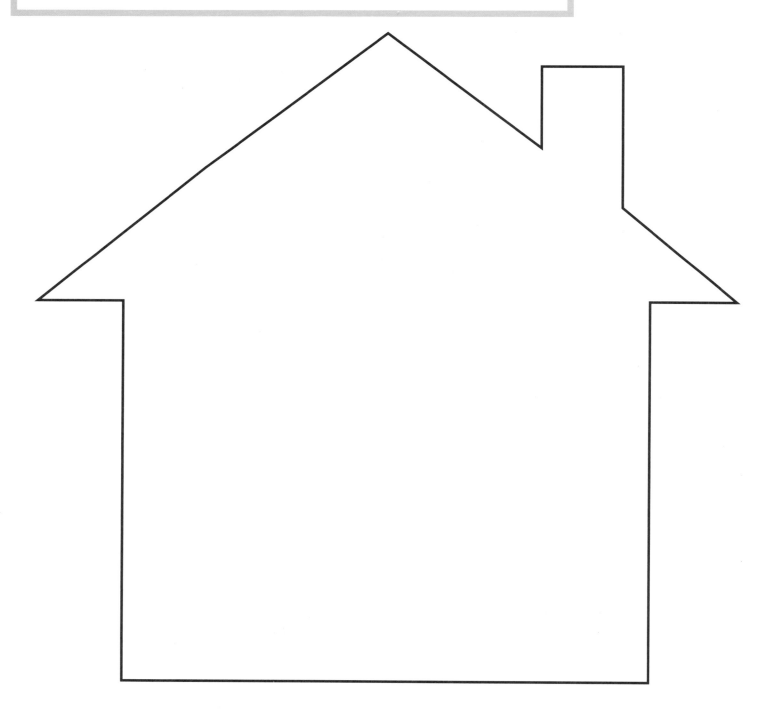

Banksy is a British artist who has never revealed his real identity. He creates art in a public way, making big bold statements about what is happening in the world, often in clever and funny ways. This is called **satire** – using humour to ridicule and expose injustice or wrongdoing. He often uses stencils to help him create his work.

INVESTIGATION

Watch a trailer for Bansky's film *Exit Through the Gift Shop.*

What does this image say to you? Is it a good message?

ACTIVITY

Create a stencil and use it in the space below. You could pick a word or image that you think might inspire people.

"IGNORANCE ALLIED w/ POWER IS THE MOST FEROCIOUS ENEMY JUSTICE CAN HAVE"
~ JAMES BALDWIN

Molly Crabapple is an illustrator who lives in New York. She draws pictures that capture some of the social injustice around her. These illustrations have appeared in important newspapers, magazines and other media, which means that they have reached a very wide audience.

In this work, Molly has created a portrait of an activist with one of their quotes.

ACTIVITY

Find an image of someone who inspires you and create a portrait of them with one of their quotes in the space here.

How could you make sure that your message reaches a wider audience? Which organisations and individuals could help you spread your ideas for change? Create a mind map below and discuss your ideas for change with your class.

INVESTIGATION

Many artists have used their art for activism: Ai Weiwei, Ms Saffaa, Maser and Shepard Fairey are just a few. They use different media and work with various organisations to help get their message out into society. Investigate and do a presentation on one of these artists.

PART B: PROCESS

ART

CRAFT

DESIGN

STRAND 1
ART

The term **art** refers to work an artist creates based on an idea they want to explore, express and/or communicate. It can be made in 2D, 3D or moving images using any media or technique and can be experienced through sight, touch, sound and sometimes smell or taste!

ACTIVITY

Create a mind map below, using sketches and words, of as many different examples of art as you can think of.

As a class, discuss your ideas and use a different colour to add any new information to your mind map above.

Do you think there is a limit to what an artwork can be?

IRISH ART

ACTIVITY

Research the Irish artists listed below and think about how they can help inspire you to create your own work. Choose one artwork by each person to look at in detail.

Artist	Describe the artwork you chose	Sketch the artwork
Mary Swanzy, Dublin Title of artwork: _____		
Francis Bacon, Dublin Title of artwork: _____		
Alice Maher, Co. Tipperary Title of artwork: _____		
Willie Doherty, Derry, Northern Ireland Title of artwork: _____		
Add another Irish artist you find interesting Artist: _____ Title of artwork: _____		

ART PROCESS: HOW AN ARTIST WORKS

An artist might begin at almost any point on this diagram. Each exploration or finished work leads, influences or informs their next creation. Drawing from primary sources is key to this process.

THINK

An artist thinks about the things that interest them. They identify ideas and do further research on these ideas, and look at the work of other artists, craftspeople and designers that interests them.

REFLECT

Review their work by questioning what went well and what they might do differently next time.

EXPLORE

They research their ideas and primary sources. They explore the art elements and design principles by experimenting with a variety of media and techniques in their drawing and making.

ART PROCESS

PRESENT

Present their finished piece to the public.

DEVELOP

Consider their ideas further through drawing, making and modifying.

REALISE

Create a finished artwork.

REFINE

Assess their work and make necessary adjustments.

Choose an artist and reflect on what process you think this artist used to create their artworks. In the art process diagram below, write the name of your chosen artist and one of their pieces of art. Fill in what you think was important to the artist on their journey from initial idea to realisation.

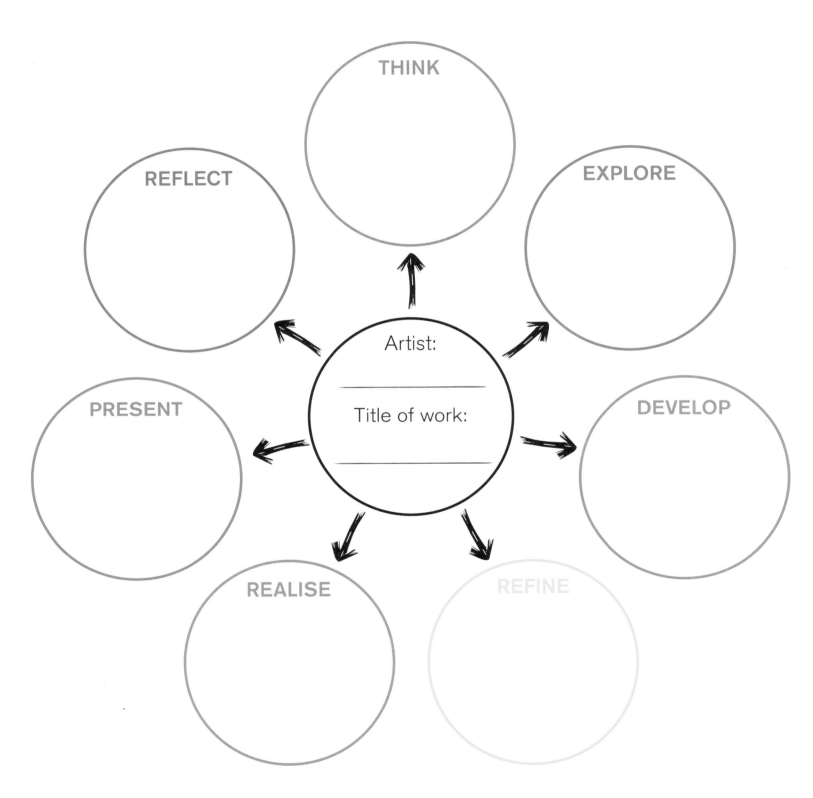

THINK

REFLECT

EXPLORE

Artist:

_____

Title of work:

_____

PRESENT

DEVELOP

REALISE

REFINE

ART STRAND PROJECT

Here is your chance to create your own artwork. First you need to select a theme. Your teacher may help you choose a theme and a technique – such as painting, sculpture or film – to work in.

ACTIVITY

Write your theme in the shape below and create a visual mind map that suggests all the ideas that are connected to your theme. In your mind map:

- ❑ Connect as many primary sources to this theme as you can think of.
- ❑ Draw a thumbnail sketch and add notes beside each primary source.
- ❑ Choose an artist you find inspiring and connect them to the theme.
- ❑ Beside the artist, list all the reasons you like their work and find them inspiring.

MY ART IDEA

ACTIVITY

Reflect on your mind map and come up with an idea for an artwork you would like to create.

My first idea (initial concept) is to create:

_____

_____

I am inspired by:

_____

_____

I plan to use:

It might look something like this (quick thumbnail sketches of idea):

_____

_____

_____

_____

_____

_____

_____

ACTIVITY

Present this first idea (initial concept) to the class group.

Record group feedback here:

_____

_____

Record your teacher's advice here:

_____

_____

_____

_____

_____

_____

Reflect on the feedback before moving on. Has the feedback encouraged you to make changes to your initial idea? You might like to make adjustments to your art idea.

PLANNING MY PROJECT

Having reflected on your initial ideas, use the feedback to help you create an artwork based on your theme (either the one you have already explored or a development of this theme).

ACTIVITY

Before you begin, sort out your ideas here:

Theme: _____

Subject matter: _____

Primary sources: _____

Technique and media: _____

Artists who inspired me: _____

How I imagine my work: _____

Start date: _____

Finish date: _____

ACTIVITY

With your teacher's help, you will set your learning intentions and success criteria for your art project. The learning intentions are important to help you reach your potential.

	LEARNING INTENTIONS	SUCCESS CRITERIA
Critical and Visual Language	I will:	I will know I have been successful if I:
Drawing	I will:	I will know I have been successful if I:
Visual Culture and Appreciation	I will:	I will know I have been successful if I:
Art Elements and Design Principles (AEDP)	I will:	I will know I have been successful if I:
Media	I will:	I will know I have been successful if I:

THINK AND EXPLORE

Try using a selection of different techniques and media to explore different art elements and design principles when drawing your primary sources.

ACTIVITY

Use these two pages to show evidence of your research using sketches, notes, pictures, photos and observations of primary sources. Explore your theme and experiment with various media.

What media do you find most fun to work with? Make a note here.

Have you labelled
your drawings
with notes?

What more can I investigate?
Check back through your Visual
Art Sketchpad.

ACTIVITY

Present these pages
of drawings/ideas to
the class and discuss.

Take feedback from your classmates and make notes below.

_____

_____

_____

_____

_____

DEVELOP AND REFINE

Develop and refine your artwork on these two pages.

How could you connect your work with the work of an artist or artists you find inspiring? Maybe you could work with similar media or ideas? Don't worry about them being exactly the same – you don't want to copy them, they just inspire you!

Keep thinking about how these ideas might become an artwork and make lots of different samples. Don't forget – you can stick photos of 3D sampling on these pages!

What developments interest you most? Are there ideas you need to think about further?

REALISE AND PRESENT

To the best of your ability, use these two pages to:

1. Complete the development of your ideas towards a fully realised artwork.

   OR

2. Complete your finished artwork or include a picture of the finished artwork here.

Remember, you can complete your artwork on these pages or separately, e.g. using watercolour paper, clay, wire, photography, film, etc.

Well done! You have created an original piece of art using the art process.

ACTIVITY

Now present your piece to your class for discussion and feedback.

Write the feedback that you receive below.

_____

_____

_____

_____

_____

REFLECT

ACTIVITY

Now that you have finished, look back on the project and evaluate your process and your realised artwork.

1. My work was successful because:

_____

_____

_____

2. I was challenged when:

_____

_____

3. But I overcame it by:

_____

_____

4. If I did this project again I would:

_____

_____

_____

5. My choices of media and techniques were appropriate because:

_____

_____

6. I managed my time by:

_____

_____

ACTIVITY

Look back at the learning intentions and success criteria that you set yourself on page 99. Reflect on whether you met these intentions.

My learning intentions	Student evaluation	Teacher feedback
I will …	I did/didn't because …	
I will …		
I will …		
I will …		
I will …		

> I have worked to the best of my ability and completed my authentic artwork.
>
> Student signature: _____
>
> Parent/guardian signature: _____
>
> Teacher signature: _____

STRAND 2
CRAFT

We use the word **craft** when a person creates an artefact that shows their artistic skills and knowledge. A craftsperson focuses on process and materials. They may choose to use traditional methods, or they may prefer to experiment with a variety of new techniques. The different skills and materials they use help to make the craftwork unique and interesting.

C&VL

ACTIVITY

Create a mind map below, using sketches and words, of as many different types of craft as you can think of.

In craft, the same primary source can be realised in a variety of different ways. Craft allows you to work with a huge variety of media using a broad range of techniques and skills.

INVESTIGATION

As a class, discuss your ideas and use a different colour to add any new information to your mind map above.

IRISH CRAFT

Research the Irish contemporary craftspeople listed below and consider how they may influence your own craftwork. Choose one craftwork by each person to look at in more detail.

Craftsperson	Describe the craftwork you chose	Sketch the craftwork
Orla Kiely Textiles Title of craftwork: _____		
Stephen Lawlor Print Title of craftwork: _____		
Alva Gallagher Glass Title of craftwork: _____		
Alan Ardiff Jewellery Title of craftwork: _____		
Add another Irish crafts- person you find interesting Craftsperson: _____ Title of craftwork: _____		

CRAFT PROCESS:
HOW A CRAFTSPERSON WORKS

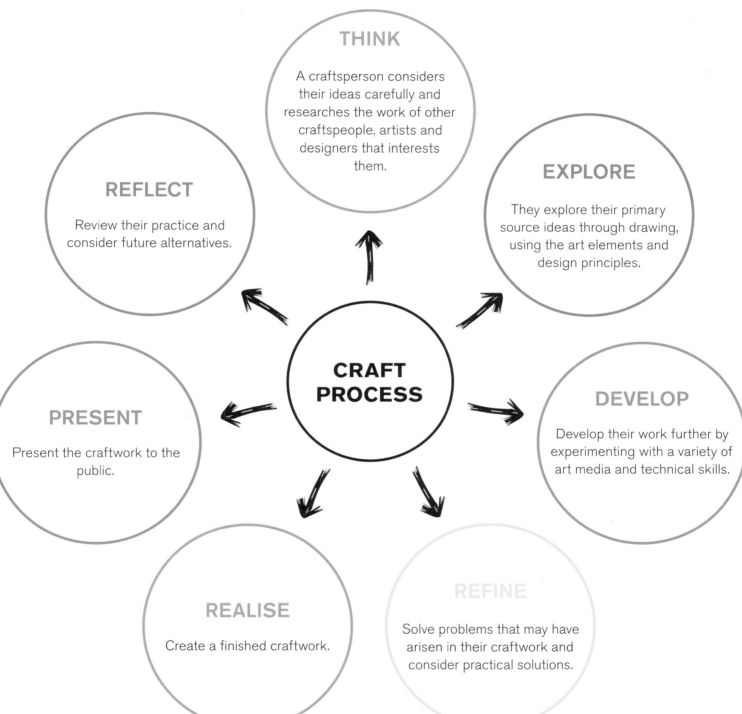

THINK

A craftsperson considers their ideas carefully and researches the work of other craftspeople, artists and designers that interests them.

EXPLORE

They explore their primary source ideas through drawing, using the art elements and design principles.

REFLECT

Review their practice and consider future alternatives.

CRAFT PROCESS

DEVELOP

Develop their work further by experimenting with a variety of art media and technical skills.

PRESENT

Present the craftwork to the public.

REALISE

Create a finished craftwork.

REFINE

Solve problems that may have arisen in their craftwork and consider practical solutions.

The craft process does not follow any particular direction. You can choose to begin at almost any point on the diagram and work from there.

Find an example of craft that interests you. In the craft process diagram below, write the name of your chosen craftsperson and one of their pieces of craft. Fill in what you think was important to the craftsperson on their journey from initial idea to realisation.

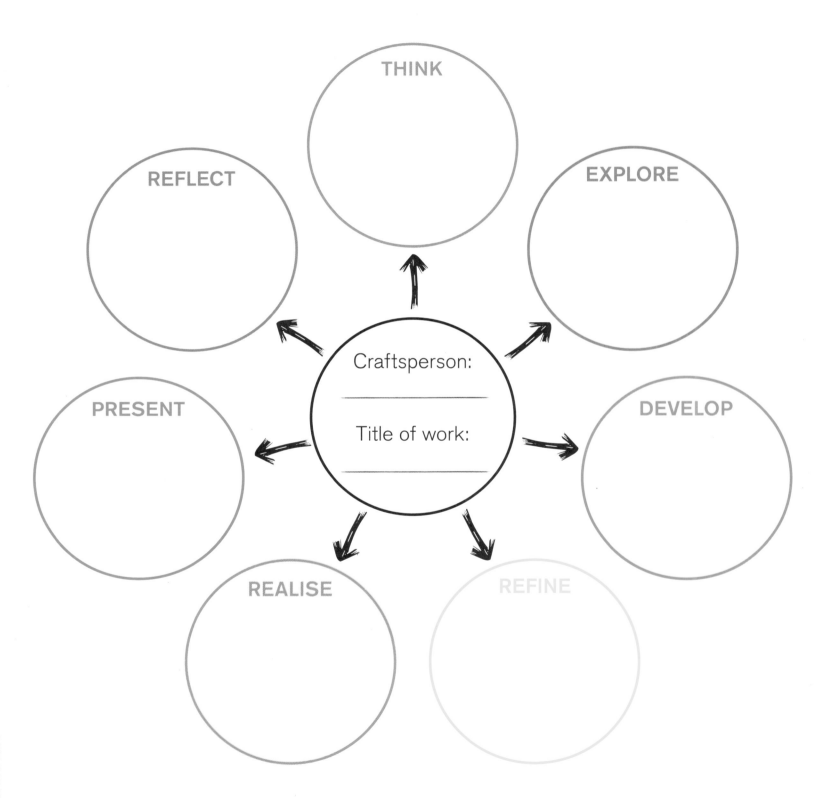

THINK

REFLECT

EXPLORE

Craftsperson:

_____

Title of work:

_____

PRESENT

DEVELOP

REALISE

REFINE

CRAFT STRAND PROJECT

Here is your chance to create your own craftwork. First you need to select a theme. Your teacher may help you choose a theme and advise you on your craft options.

Write your theme in the shape below and create a visual mind map that suggests all the ideas that are connected to your theme. In your mind map:

- ❏ Connect as many primary sources to this theme as you can think of.
- ❏ Draw a thumbnail sketch and add notes to support each primary source.
- ❏ Choose a craftsperson you find inspiring and connect them to the theme.
- ❏ Beside the craftsperson's name, list all the reasons you like their work and find them inspiring.

MY CRAFT IDEA

Reflect on your mind map and come up with an idea for a craftwork you would like to create.

My first idea (initial concept) is to create:

_____

_____

I am inspired by:

_____

_____

I plan to use:

_____

_____

_____

_____

_____

_____

_____

It might look something like this (quick thumbnail sketches of idea):

ACTIVITY

Present this first idea (initial concept) to the class group.

Record group feedback here:

_____

_____

Record your teacher's advice here:

_____

_____

_____

_____

_____

_____

_____

_____

Reflect on the feedback before moving on. Has the feedback encouraged you to make changes to your initial idea? You might like to make adjustments to your craft idea.

PLANNING MY PROJECT

Reflect on your initial ideas and use the feedback to help you create a craftwork based on your theme (either the one you have already explored or a development of this theme).

ACTIVITY

Before you begin, sort out your ideas here.

Type of craft: _____

Theme: _____

Subject matter: _____

Primary sources: _____

Technique and media: _____

Craftspeople who inspired me: _____

How I imagine my work: _____

Start date: _____

Finish date: _____

ACTIVITY

With your teacher's help, you will set your learning intentions and success criteria for your craft project. The learning intentions are important to help you reach your potential.

	LEARNING INTENTIONS	SUCCESS CRITERIA
Critical and Visual Language	I will:	I will know I have been successful if I:
Drawing	I will:	I will know I have been successful if I:
Visual Culture and Appreciation	I will:	I will know I have been successful if I:
Art Elements and Design Principles (AEDP)	I will:	I will know I have been successful if I:
Media	I will:	I will know I have been successful if I:

THINK AND EXPLORE

Remember to use your imagination as one of your primary sources.

ACTIVITY

Use these two pages to show evidence of your research using sketches, notes, pictures, photos and observations of primary sources. Explore your theme and experiment with various media.

Experiment with media to help you explore the art elements and design principles throughout the craft process. When you use 3D media it can be recorded and stuck into the book.

Begin to connect your drawings to your theme and include notes.

ACTIVITY

Present these pages of drawings/ideas to the class and discuss.

Take feedback from your classmates and make notes below.

_____

_____

_____

_____

_____

DEVELOP AND REFINE

Remember to include examples of craft materials you have used. Don't forget – you can also stick photos of 3D sampling into the book.

Throughout the craft process it is important to record examples of craft techniques you have used.

Is there anything you need to do to develop the function of your craft?

What media did you find linked best to your chosen craft?

REALISE AND PRESENT

Now use these two pages to:
1. Complete your finished 2D craftwork/proposal for craft.
   OR
2. Glue photos of your completed 3D craftwork onto both pages.

You can complete your craftwork here or create it using your chosen craft media and photograph the final artefact.

Well done! You have created an original piece of craft using the craft process.

ACTIVITY

Now present your piece to your class for discussion and feedback.

Write the feedback that you receive below.

_____

_____

_____

_____

_____

_____

REFLECT

ACTIVITY

Now that you have finished, look back on the project and evaluate your process and your realised craftwork.

1. My work was successful because:

_____

_____

_____

2. I was challenged when:

_____

_____

3. But I overcame it by:

_____

_____

4. If I did this project again I would:

_____

_____

5. My choices of media and techniques were appropriate because:

_____

_____

6. I managed my time by:

_____

_____

ACTIVITY

Look back at the learning intentions and success criteria that you set yourself on page 113. Reflect on whether you met your intentions.

My learning intentions	Student evaluation	Teacher feedback
I will …	I did/didn't because …	
I will …		
I will …		
I will …		
I will …		

I have worked to the best of my ability and completed my authentic artwork.

Student signature: _____

Parent/guardian signature: _____

Teacher signature: _____

STRAND 3
DESIGN

Design is the process of problem-solving, planning and creating. Design is what links creativity and innovation. It is user-centred; great designers care a lot about the people who will use the product, service, building or experience they are developing. They imagine, they research and they make, often collaborating with other specialists during this process.

ACTIVITY

Create a mind map below, using sketches and words, of as many different examples of design in your environment as you can think of.

INVESTIGATION

As a class, discuss your ideas and use a different colour to add any new information to your mind map above.

Consider the work of engineers, architects, and graphic, fashion, industrial and interior designers.

IRISH DESIGN

Research the Irish designers listed below to help inspire your own work. Choose one design by each designer and describe and draw it in the boxes below.

Designer	Describe the design	Sketch the design
Josie MacAvin Set Designer and Art Director Title of design: _____		
Consolata Boyle Costume Designer Title of design: _____		
Philip Treacy Milliner Title of design: _____		
Kevin Roche Architect Title of design: _____		
Add another Irish designer you find interesting Designer: _____ Title of design: _____		

DESIGN PROCESS:
HOW A DESIGNER WORKS

THINK

Designers look at the world around them and think about ways of improving it through better design and new inventions.

REFLECT

This stage is the opportunity for the designer to evaluate their process to see how they can improve it in future.

EXPLORE

They explore what other designers have done and look for inspiration from other disciplines.

PRESENT

The new design is launched and presented to the public.

DESIGN PROCESS

DEVELOP

They develop their ideas and experiment with a variety of materials to create a prototype.

REALISE

The realisation stage is when the design is resolved and completed.

REFINE

At this stage, the designer trials the prototype and looks for feedback on how to improve the design.

Choose a designer and think about the process this designer might have used to create their design. In the design process diagram below, write the name of your chosen designer and the title of one of their designs. Fill in what you think was important to the designer on their journey from initial idea to realisation.

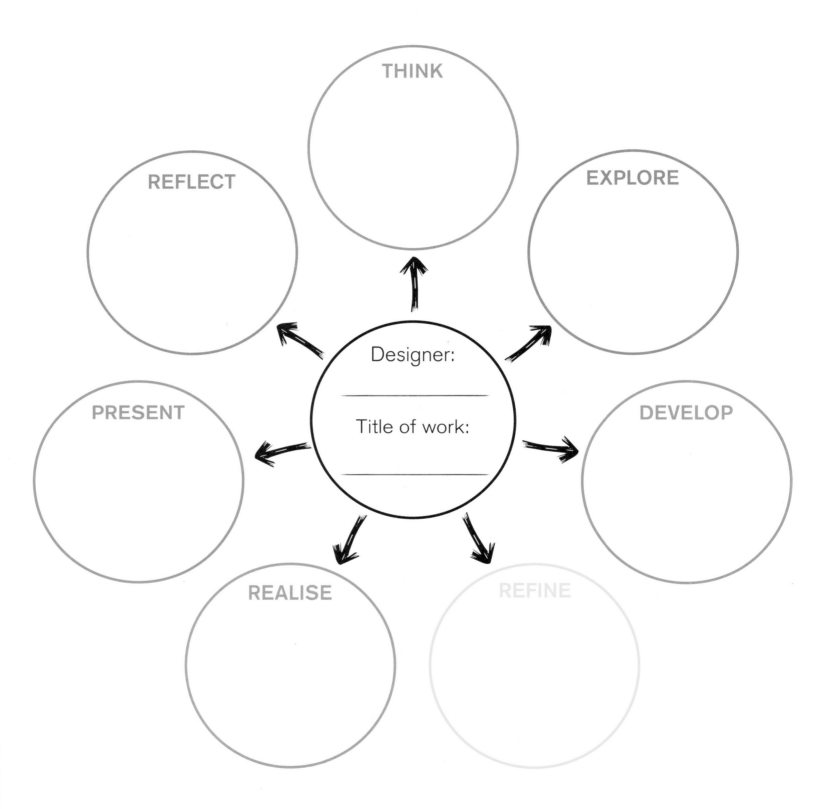

THINK

REFLECT

EXPLORE

Designer:

_____

Title of work:

_____

PRESENT

DEVELOP

REALISE

REFINE

DESIGN STRAND PROJECT

Here is your chance to create your own design. Designers often work to a design brief or in response to a need or a situation. Your teacher will help you to select a theme and may give you other instructions for your design project – this is your design brief.

STRAND 3: DESIGN / **125**

ACTIVITY

Write your design brief in the shape below and create a visual mind map of your ideas that are connected to your brief. In your mind map:

- ❏ Connect as many primary sources to this theme as you can think of.
- ❏ Draw a thumbnail sketch and add notes beside each primary source.
- ❏ Choose a designer you find inspiring and connect them to the theme.
- ❏ Beside the designer's name, list all the reasons you like their work and find them inspiring.

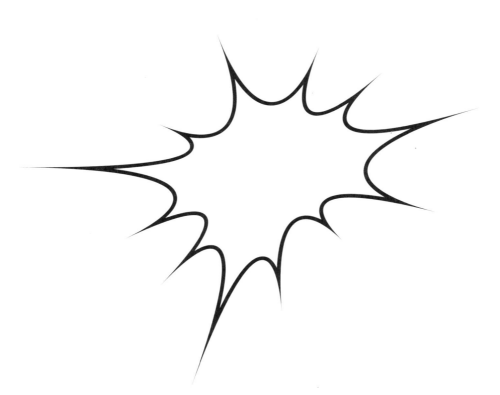

MY DESIGN IDEA

Reflect on your mind map and come up with an idea for a design you would like to create.

My first idea (initial concept) is to create:

_____

_____

I am inspired by:

_____

_____

I plan to use:

_____

_____

_____

_____

_____

_____

_____

It might look something like this (quick thumbnail sketches of idea):

ACTIVITY

Present this first idea (initial concept) to the class group.

Record group feedback here:

_____

_____

Record your teacher's advice here:

_____

_____

_____

_____

_____

_____

_____

Reflect on the feedback before moving on. Has the feedback encouraged you to make changes to your initial idea? You might like to make adjustments to your design idea.

PLANNING MY PROJECT

Reflect on your initial ideas, and use the feedback to help you create a design based on your theme (either the one you have already explored or a development of this theme).

Theme: _____

Subject matter: _____

Primary sources: _____

Technique and media: _____

Designers who inspired me: _____

How I imagine my work: _____

Start date: _____

Finish date: _____

ACTIVITY

With your teacher's help, you will set your learning intentions and success criteria for your design project. The learning intentions are important to help you reach your potential.

	LEARNING INTENTIONS	SUCCESS CRITERIA
Critical and Visual Language	I will:	I will know I have been successful if I:
Drawing	I will:	I will know I have been successful if I:
Visual Culture and Appreciation	I will:	I will know I have been successful if I:
Art Elements and Design Principles (AEDP)	I will:	I will know I have been successful if I:
Media	I will:	I will know I have been successful if I:

THINK AND EXPLORE

ACTIVITY

Use these two pages to show evidence of your research using sketches, notes, pictures, photos and observations of primary sources. Explore your theme and experiment with various media.

Are you investigating your primary sources by using a selection of different media and techniques for each art element and design principle?

What media did you find most fun to work with?

Have you labelled your drawings?

ACTIVITY

Present these pages of drawings/ideas to the class and discuss.

Take feedback from your classmates and make notes below.

_____

_____

_____

_____

_____

_____

_____

Look back over these pages. What more can you investigate?

DEVELOP AND REFINE

ACTIVITY

Develop your design on these two pages. Make any additions or subtractions you think it might benefit from. Is there any way you could simplify the design? Does it need something extra?

Keep thinking about how these ideas might become a finished design and make lots of different samples. Don't forget that you can stick photos of 3D sampling on these pages!

Reflect on your drawings of primary sources. How could you connect your favourites with the work of a designer you find inspiring?

Are there ideas you need to think about further?

What developments are most interesting to you?

REALISE AND PRESENT

ACTIVITY

To the best of your ability, use these two pages to:

1. Complete the development of your ideas, refining them into a fully realised design.
   OR
2. Complete your finished design on these pages or include a picture of the design here.

You can complete your design on these pages or separately, e.g. if you create a 3D item you could take a photograph of it and stick it here.

Well done! You have created an original piece of design using the design process.

ACTIVITY

Now present your design to your class for discussion and feedback.

Write the feedback that you receive below.

_____

_____

_____

_____

REFLECT

ACTIVITY

Now that you have finished, look back at the original design brief and think about how the project went. Evaluate your process and your realised design.

1. My work was successful because:

_____

_____

_____

2. I was challenged when:

_____

_____

3. But I overcame it by:

_____

_____

4. If I did this project again I would:

_____

_____

_____

5. My choices of media and techniques were appropriate because:

_____

_____

6. I managed my time by:

_____

_____

ACTIVITY

Look back at the learning intentions and success criteria that you set yourself on page 127. Reflect on whether you met these intentions.

My learning intentions	Student evaluation	Teacher feedback
I will …	I did/didn't because …	
I will …		
I will …		
I will …		
I will …		

I have worked to the best of my ability and completed my authentic artwork.

Student signature: _____

Parent/guardian signature: _____

Teacher signature: _____

AN INTRODUCTION TO THE CLASSROOM-BASED ASSESSMENTS

What is a CBA?

A CBA is a Classroom-Based Assessment where your teacher will assess a specific classroom task. You will need to complete two CBAs during your Junior Cycle Visual Art course – one in Second Year and one in Third Year. At least one of your realised artworks in art, craft or design must be 3D.

Second Year

What will I do in CBA 1: *Process to Realisation?*

This is your first Classroom-Based Assessment and it takes place in Second Year. Using the Visual Art Process of THINKING, EXPLORING, DEVELOPING, REFINING, REALISING, PRESENTING and REFLECTING, you will complete a task that has been given to you by your Art teacher.

You will be given a choice of themes to work from and you will explore your theme individually or in groups through one of the strands: Art, Craft or Design. Your teacher will help you choose your theme and strand, and will guide you through the Visual Art Process. Throughout the process, you will work directly from primary sources and explore your initial ideas using research and development. It is important that you use the five elements of Visual Art throughout your work and record the process in your Visual Art Sketchpad. When you have completed your realised artwork, you can then reflect on your decisions, process and the wonderful work you have created. The CBA is nothing to be scared of; remember, you have your **Art Odyssey** Sketchpad to refer to and guide you on your next creative journey! You will be awarded a descriptor of achievement by your Art teacher for your Classroom-Based Assessment 1.

Third Year

PHASE 1

What will I do in CBA 2: *Communicate and Reflect?*

At the beginning of Third Year, you will be issued with a 'Visual Art Project Brief for Classroom-Based Assessment 2 and the Final Assessment' by the State Examinations Commission. This will contain all your instructions and a selection of themes to choose from. Using the Visual Art Process of THINKING, EXPLORING, DEVELOPING, REFINING, REALISING, PRESENTING and REFLECTING, you will work directly from primary sources as you did in CBA 1. Your teacher will guide you through the two strands through which you will be creating your realised artworks in Phase 2. It is important for you to engage with the five elements of Visual Art as you research and develop your initial idea, and record and annotate your work in your Visual Art Sketchpad. Your Visual Art Sketchpad will also help you to present your ideas and the development of your theme to your Art class and teacher. It is important to use your Visual Art Sketchpad to record and reflect on the feedback you have been given as you will need this for your final assessment. You will be awarded a descriptor of achievement by your Art teacher for your Class-Based Assessment 2.

PHASE 2

What is the State-Certified Final Assessment?

This takes place towards the end of Third Year. It is a continuation of your CBA 2: *Communicate and Reflect*. Based on your reflection of the feedback you have received in CBA 2, you will develop the work based on your chosen theme further and create two realised artworks. You will be issued with and work directly into your State Examinations Commissions Workbook. The workbook and the two realised artworks will be assessed by an external examiner in your school.

Your teacher will go through these instructions with you and guide you through CBA 1, CBA 2 and the Final Assessment.

GLOSSARY

Below are definitions of the key words used throughout your Visual Art Sketchpad. There is space at the end for you to add other key words you have learned along the way.

Highlight the art elements and design principles in colour.

Analogous colours: These colours sit beside each other on the colour wheel. They are harmonious.

Asymmetry: When things are different on either side and have no central axis. This unbalances a work and draws attention to one side more than the other.

Balance: Describes how we create visual weight in a composition to show stability or tension.

Collage: Making use of collected items (e.g. papers, magazine clippings) to create a new image.

Colour: The word we use to describe how our eyes see light.

Complementary colours: The colours opposite each other on the colour wheel. They bring out the brightness in each other.

Composition: The word we use to describe how we *compose* or arrange what is in a picture (our **subject matter**).

Continuous drawing: A drawing technique where the pen or pencil isn't lifted from the page until the drawing is finished.

Contour drawing: A drawing that describes the edge or outline of an object.

Contrast: The arrangement of objects/subjects that are opposite to each other, e.g. light and dark, big and small.

Cross hatching: A drawing technique created by crossing lines. It is used to create tone.

Dot: The first mark on the page and the end of a line. A dot can be used in many ways. You can use a dot to start a line, add tone to show shadow, or to create visual texture when you are doing observation drawing.

Figurative art: Art that shows recognisable objects – but the objects don't have to be displayed realistically.

Foreshortening: When an object looks squashed or compressed from a distance because perspective is distorting it.

Form: The 3D shape of an object on a 2D surface.

Gestural drawing: A quick drawing style that captures the essence of a subject.

Harmony: How an object or image is visually balanced – a harmonious image feels calm.

Highlight: Where the light hits an object and creates reflection or brightness. Artists use it with shadow to help indicate form and perspective.

Human-made object: Any non-natural object made by people.

Imaginative drawing: Drawing from your imagination – you aren't drawing directly from a primary or secondary source.

Layout: How an image is organised – where objects and text (if used) are placed. It affects hierarchy and harmony in an image.

Light: The word we use to describe areas of brightness as well as areas of light to dark tones.

Line: A point moving in or through space, like a pathway. It can move in any direction.

Mark-making: A term used to describe marks and patterns made with art media.

Medium/media (pl.): Art materials – anything from pencil to paint to clay …

Monochromatic: Something using only one colour (but it can have different shades of that colour).

Montage: An image made up of collected/cut-out images.

Natural object: An object from nature (not human-made).

Negative space: Cut-out, empty space or background space.

Palette: The group of colours used in an artwork, or the surface an artist uses to mix colours.

Pattern: A repetition of shapes in an image or design.

Perspective: A drawing technique that conveys an impression of distance, space and scale.

Pigment: Pure colour.

Pointillism: A painting technique that uses small dots of colour.

Portrait: An image of a face.

Positive space: Filled-in space. It refers to the main focus of an image.

Primary colours: The three basic colours – red, yellow and blue. They are the basis of all other colours on the colour wheel.

Primary source: An object, person or space that an artist directly uses as a reference when creating an artwork.

Proportion: How an object, person or space is made up in relation to itself and its surroundings.

Scale: The size of one thing in relation to another.

Secondary colours: Orange, green and purple. They are made by mixing two primary colours.

Shade: The depiction of shadow in a drawing.

Shape: 2D shapes are flat and have straight or curved lines as their edge. 3D shapes are solid and they have height, width and depth.

Space: The distance between people, places or objects in an artwork.

Still-life: The arrangement of objects that cannot move by themselves in an artwork.

Subject matter: The physical objects/subjects in an artwork.

Symmetry: A mirror image – or how each side of an image reflects the other.

Tension: An imbalance in a work of art, craft or design.

Tertiary colours: Made by mixing a primary and secondary colour together.

Texture: The feel of an object.

Theme: The main idea that an artwork is based on or is about, e.g. love or war.

Tint: Adding white to a colour to lighten it.

Tone: The word used to describe the way that light falls on a 3D object. The part of the object on which the light is strongest are **highlights** and the darker areas are shadows.

Typeface: A specific lettering design, often called a font.

Typography: The art and design of lettering.

Vanishing point: The point where all lines appear to meet in a perspective drawing.

Add your new key words here:

_____

_____

_____

_____

_____

_____

_____